THE AUDUBON NATURE ENCYCLOPEDIA

THE AUDUBON NATURE ENCYCLOPEDIA

SPONSORED BY THE NATIONAL AUDUBON SOCIETY

VOLUME 8

CURTIS BOOKS
A division of
The Curtis Publishing Company
Philadelphia – New York

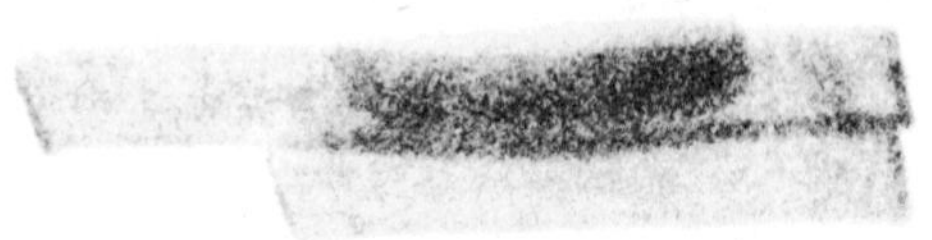

CREATED AND PRODUCED BY
COPYLAB PUBLISHING COUNSEL, INC., NEW YORK

First Printing
 Library of Congress Card Catalog Number 64-8877.

Published simultaneously in Canada by
Curtis Distributing Company, Ltd., Toronto.

Printed in the United States of America

PICTORIAL ACKNOWLEDGMENTS, Volume 8

Arthur W. Ambler*, VIII, 1447 —Roger T. Peterson*, 1395,1400,1413,1424, 1448 —Bruce Horsfall,1396—Thase Daniels*,1398—John H.Gerard*,1399, 1410, 1474, 1532 left, 1545 bottom —Allan D. Cruickshank*, 1401, 1412, 1415, 1421, 1430 bottom, 1432, 1435, 1449, 1451,1452,1466 bottom, 1469 1494, 1526, 1535, 1536 left, 1572, 1574-75, 1578 —Lee Adams, 1402, 1470, 1564 —W. D. Berry, 1403, 1571 —Karl W. Kenyon*, 1405 —Allan Brooks, 1406, 1495, 1496 —Alfred M. Bailey*, 1407 —G. E. Kirkpatrick*, 1408 —H. A. Thornhill*, 1409 —D. Muir*, 1414 —Henry Gilbert*, 1417 —S. A. Grimes*, 1418 top —G. Roland Austing*, 1418 bottom —Leonard Lee Rue, III*, 1427, 1466 top —Lena Scott Harris, 1428, 1433, 1445, 1454, 1455, 1467, 1568, 1569 —Lynwood M. Chace*, 1429, 1545 top —Michael H.Bevans,1430,1437,1440,1446,1484,1485,1486,1488,1490,1491 bottom, 1493, 1543 —Clarence J. Hylander*, 1439, 1507 bottom right —Tom McHugh*, 1443 —Karl H. Maslowski*, 1444, 1566, 1587 —New York State Conservationist, 1456 top, 1476, 1500-01 —United States Department of Agriculture, 1456 bottom, 1546, 1549 bottom,1552—Robert C. Hermes*, 1457 —Alfred O. Gross*, 1458 —Robert Jackowitz, 1462 —Eliot Porter*,1463—Walter Ferguson,1464,1465 —Helen Cruickshank*, 1472 —Thomas Eberhard*, 1473 —John K. Terres, 1477, 1478, 1530, 1531, 1560 —Art Bilsten*, 1483 —National Park Service, 1491 top, 1507 bottom left —American Museum of Natural History, 1497, 1498, 1503, 1509, 1510, 1558, 1559 —Hugh Spencer*, 1506 top, 1507 top left, top right, 1541 —Grant M. Haist*, 1506 bottom —Roland C. Clement, 1512, 1513, 1561 —Brooklyn Botanical Garden, 1515, 1518 —Hal Harrison*, 1519 top —Rowena Taxersalm*, 1519 bottom —Robert Seibert, 1520-21, 1528-29, 1533 right —Soil Conservation Service, 1532 right, 1533 top —Harold Mayfield, 1534 —Charles J. Ott*, 1536 right —Lewis W. Walker*, 1537, 1592 —Verna R. Johnston*, 1538 —N. E. Beck, Jr.*, 1542 bottom —W. Treat Davidson*, 1549 top —Van Dersal, 1556 (courtesy of United States Soil Conservation Service) —George Porter*, 1563, 1583, 1584, 1585 —United States Fish and Wildlife Service, 1570 —Wilford C. Miller*, 1573, 1591 —Hugh Halliday*, 1576 —Olin S. Pettingill, Jr.*, 1580 —United States Forest Service, 1581 —Robert H. Wright, 1589

*Photographs from Photo-Film Department of National Audubon Society

Baltimore oriole

ORIOLE

The meadowlark, blackbird, oriole family (Icteridae) is chiefly tropical, and is well represented in Central and South America by troupials, oropendolas, caciques, and a wide variety of orioles. Four of these essentially tropical orioles venture into the United States, three along the Mexican border, and one as a new immigrant into South Florida.

The hooded oriole, *Icterus cucullatus,* breeding from southern California east to the Rio Grande Valley and south, is the only western oriole with an orange crown. Only the face, back, wings, and tail of the male are black. The female resembles the female Bullock's oriole, but is completely yellow underneath, with no white.

Scott's oriole, *Icterus parisorum,* with the same territory as the hooded oriole, has the black head and back of the Baltimore oriole, a black tail tip, and lemon yellow back and underparts. The female is greener than other female orioles. The black-headed oriole, *Icterus graduacauda,* of the lower Rio Grande Valley, has a yellow back, and the sexes are similar.

The spotted-breasted oriole, *Icterus pectoralis,* native to Mexico and Costa Rica, has recently become established in Miami. Both sexes are brilliant orange on the head and black on the back.
—G.B.S.

Baltimore Oriole
Other Common Names—Golden robin, hangnest, firebird
Scientific Name—*Icterus galbula*
Family—Icteridae (meadowlarks, blackbirds, and orioles)
Order—Passeriformes
Size—Length, 7½ inches
Range—Breeds east of the Rocky Mountains from Nova Scotia, southern Ontario, Manitoba, Saskatchewan, and Alberta, south to northern Alabama and northern Georgia. It is a rare bird, even in migration, along the southern Atlantic Coast and in Florida

The male Baltimore oriole is a brilliant orange and black. He arrives first in the northern nesting area and repeats his whistled song throughout the day. It is an announcement that this is his territory. Any other male oriole that trespasses on his territory is chased away. Three or four days, or a week later, the female arrives. She is less flaming than her mate, but with enough of his pattern and appearance to be recognized.

In building their nest, Baltimore orioles are accomplished "craftsmen." The nest is suspended like a hanging basket or a purse. The drooping tips of elm branches make the best supports, because cats and squirrels will rarely trust their weight to the slender twigs. Elm trees are used most often, but occasionally other trees may be used (*See Elm*).

It takes about a week to complete the nest. It is a beautiful creation. The first part of its construction is probably the most difficult—tying the long fibers to the twigs, making the loops, and shaping the framework of the basket. Much of the weaving is done from the inside, and a thin lining of hair and feathers is often added just before the eggs are laid.

The four to six eggs are as beautiful as those of any bird. They are covered with scrawls and scratches. After two weeks of incubation by the female, the eggs hatch. In another two weeks, the young are ready to leave the nest. The male, which usually takes little part in incubation, takes an active part in their feeding. His piping song is silenced, and he spends all his time searching for food for his young—beetles, plant lice, and caterpillars. Nearly seven-eights of the oriole's food is made up of insects. When the young leave the nest, they keep up an almost constant pleading for food.

Baltimore oriole's can be attracted to the yard with feeders containing a honey-water mixture, similar to that which lures hummingbirds. Also, they will sip juice from orange halves that are placed

Baltimore orioles from Audubon's Elephant Folio

on feeding trays. Both adults undergo a molt before starting south but instead of changing to a duller dress, the male replaces his old feathers for ones equally as brilliant. This plumage seems to be more in keeping with the glare of the tropics than are the duller winter colors of the male tanagers.

By mid-September most Baltimore orioles have left their breeding territories, but some stragglers stay later, even into winter on rare occasions. There are several records of Baltimore orioles having wintered as far north as the New England states. However it is rare, even in migration, along the south Atlantic Coast and in Florida. It migrates through eastern Mexico to its winter home in Central and South America.

—A.B., Jr.

Bullock's Oriole
Other Common Names—None
Scientific Name—*Icterus bullockii*
Family—Icteridae (meadowlarks, blackbirds, and orioles)
Order—Passeriformes
Size—Length, 8 inches
Range—Southwestern Canada, Montana, southwestern North Dakota and central South Dakota, south to northern Baja California and Veracruz. Winters from southern Mexico to Costa Rica west of continental divide

Bullock's oriole, male (above); female (below)

Like a flame, Bullock's oriole flashes through the cottonwoods that cluster about the ranch houses. Although there are other orioles in the arid southwest, this is the only one familiar to most westerners. Arriving late in March, April, or May, according to the particular locality, the male announces himself with an accented piping song *kip, kip-kip tew, whit-wheen whit, kip,* or a chatter which is also given by the female. When she arrives they swing a feltlike hammock from a willow, cottonwood, tall oak, or sycamore, usually near a stream, pond, or an irrigation ditch. It is the western counterpart of the Baltimore oriole so typical of elm-shaded streets in eastern towns, but differs in having a black crown and orange cheeks and an orange line above the eye. The female has a whiter belly than the females of most other orioles. After the young are fledged in July or early August the family roves together for a very short time—and by September all but a few stragglers have gone south again. As a spring migrant it is found in many types of habitats.

Adult male orchard oriole (top); young male (middle); female (bottom)

Orchard Oriole
Other Common Names—Brown oriole, basket bird
Scientific Name—*Icterus spurius*
Family—Icteridae (meadowlarks, blackbirds, and orioles)
Order—Passeriformes
Size—Length, 7¼inches
Range—Southern Manitoba and Ontario, Minnesota, Wisconsin, Michigan east to central eastern New York, northeastern Massachusetts and north-central Pennsylvania, North Dakota, South Dakota south to central Nebraska and northeastern Colorado. South through central, northern, and western Texas to Mexico also the Gulf Coast of northern Florida. Winters from southern Mexico south to Colombia

The orchard oriole is a persistent singer, and during the nesting season lively melody is heard continually, even during the heat of midday. Sometimes it sings on the wing, but only when passing rapidly from one treetop to another.

The orchard oriole is not, as one might judge from its name, exclusively an inhabitant of the orchard, but is equally at home among the shade trees about the house or along streets, especially in the thick foliage of Norway spruces frequently planted about lawns. Always during the breeding season, however, the orchard oriole is distinctly a bird of cultivated land immediately about man's habitation, rather than of the wilder, wooded country. When the nesting cares are over the orioles scatter more widely, and little family parties foraging along the fence-roads and edges of the woods, far from house or garden, are often seen. Originally, before there were any orchards to lure it away, the orchard oriole was an inhabitant of wooded riverbanks.

It is not easy to see a singing orchard oriole, since it clings closely to the shelter offered by the dense foliage of the treetops. Now and then however, one flies rapidly from one favorite feeding spot to another, or back to the nest tree. As it comes suddenly into view on one of these flights it always seems smaller than one would expect; probably the volume of its song, or familiarity with its relative, the Baltimore oriole, leads one to picture this bird as larger than it really is.

The food of the orchard orioles consists largely of caterpillars and other insects that are found among the treetops. Now and then, especially after the breeding season, an individual alights in an open field, often on plowed ground, in search of the insects that lurk there. In late summer, when the family groups go foraging about the country, berries of various kinds seem to constitute a large portion of their food.

One observer has noted that "few birds do more good and less harm than our orchard oriole, especially to the fruit-grower. The bulk of its food consists of small beetles, plant lice, flies, hairless caterpillars, cabbage worms, grasshoppers, rose bugs, and larvae of all kinds, while the few berries it may help itself to during the short time they last are many times paid for in the greater number of noxious insects destroyed; and it certainly deserves the fullest protection."

The nest of the orchard oriole is usually supported upon slender twigs in the top of an apple tree. It is somewhat pensile, but much shorter and more rigid than the long, pocketlike nest of the Baltimore oriole; in fact, it is usually nearly spherical, with the opening somewhat constricted. It is made of fine, dry, greenish or yellow grasses, elaborately woven and lined, especially on the bottom, with soft vegetable down from thistle-blooms, buttonwood seeds, and other plants. A carefully unwound single strand of grass from one of these nests was 13 inches long, and had been looped through the other strands 34 times. The eggs are grayish-white with lavender spots, blackish blotches, and pen marks

A female orchard oriole feeds her hungry offspring

The orchard oriole expertly weaves a deeply cupped nest of grasses

and are thus similar to those of the Baltimore oriole, but smaller and more coarsely marked. They number three to five, and measure four-fifths by three-fifths of an inch.

The plumage of the male orchard oriole is subject to striking changes as the bird passes from nestling to adult, and these proved very puzzling to the early ornithologists. In fact, it was left for that painstaking student, Alexander Wilson, to explain properly the several plumages of this bird. The old male is chestnut-and-black while the female at all times wears olive-and-yellow plumage. The male in its nestling plumage, and during the first autumn, is similar to the adult female; but by the next spring it has acquired a black throat. Often one nest is attended by a black-throated , olive-green male, while the proprietor of the next is clad in chestnut-and-black.

To add to the complication, some of the olive-green males have a part of the tail feathers black, and have black-and-chestnut spots on other parts of the body. Some ornithologists are of the opinion that these birds are in the second-year breeding plumage, while the black-and-chestnut birds are in the third; but it seems probable that they represent merely individual variations, and that all the males are in the black-and-chestnut dress by their second nesting season.

At any rate, the male orchard oriole is a good example of the interesting problems that are encountered in the study of sequence of plumages and molting. Similar differences between breeding males of the first and second year may be detected in other species, but are not usually so pronounced. The Baltimore oriole is much duller the first year, and the scarlet tanager and rose-breasted grosbeak have olive or brown wing and tail feathers, instead of black ones. All these changes, too, are brought about by a molt or renewal of the feathers, either in the late summer after the breeding season or in the early spring. The feathers themselves do not change color, so that wherever changes of plumage such as those take place, they are produced by replacement of feathers of one color by those of another. —W.S.

OSAGE ORANGE (*See under Mulberry*)

A pair of ospreys tend their young in a crude nest of sticks and roots

OSPREY
Other Common Names—Fish hawk
Scientific Name—*Pandion haliaetus*
Family—Pandionidae (ospreys)
Order—Falconiformes
Size—Length , 23 inches
Range—Cosmopolitan, along seacoasts and large bodies of water in temperate and tropical areas of all continents. In New World from northern Canada south to Gulf Coast, British Honduras, and western Mexico. South in winter to Argentina.

The osprey, or fish hawk, is fairly common along seacoasts and about the lakes and watercourses of interior regions. It is a bird of splendid appearance and lends a touch of interest to the landscape in whatever regions it inhabits. It feeds entirely upon fishes which it catches in its powerful talons. Leisurely winging its way over the water, it keeps a sharp watch for such quarry as may be seen just beneath the surface. Once a fish is sighted, it descends with great speed and force, making a prodigious plunge and splash and usually emerges with its silvery prey.

The osprey should not be regarded as detrimental to man's interests for it nowhere exists in sufficient numbers to have any appreciable effect upon the supply of fishes. Then, too, by far the larger number caught have no value for human consumption (*See Fish-eating Birds*).

The osprey is found nesting both solitarily and in colonies. The best known colony is at Gardiner's Island off the eastern end of Long Island, New York where as many as 200 nests have been counted. The nest is a huge affair, usually in trees, but sometimes on cliffs or on the ground. From two to four eggs are laid. These usually are heavily marked with chocolate-colored blotches.

There has been a notable decline in the osprey's numbers in the years since insecticides such as DDT and its derivatives came into widespread usage.

Roger Tory Peterson, American orni-

The feet of the osprey are specialized for grasping its slippery prey

thologist, has explained the far-reaching effects of these persistent poisons in the following way: "Traces of poisons ingested by little fish upriver—either in the runoff or through poisoned insects—make them easier prey for larger fish. Numbers of affected fingerlings compound their poisons in the predators, and it is the large fish that is wobbly, swimming near the surface, that is most likely to be caught by the osprey, which transfers the accumulated poisons to its own tissues. Natural selection becomes unnatural selection." (*See DDT*).

In 1954 a large nesting colony of ospreys totaling some 300 birds was located at the mouth of the Connecticut River on the eastern coast of the United States. By 1964, just 10 years later, only 15 breeding pairs could be found. At this rate it is estimated that the last ospreys will disappear from Connecticut in 1970 or 1971 (*See also under Eagle*).

An analysis of osprey eggs that failed to hatch revealed significant amounts of DDT, DDE, and other pesticides. Thirty samples of fish taken from osprey nests contained the poisons.

Oswego tea

OSWEGO TEA

Other Common Names—Bee balm
Scientific Name—*Monarda didyma*
Family—Labiatae (mint family)
Range—New York to Michigan, south, chiefly in the uplands, to Georgia and Tennessee; escaped from cultivation east to Quebec, New England, Long Island, and New Jersey
Habitat—Rich woods, thickets, and bottomlands
Time of Blooming—Late June to August

This member of the mint family has a terminal cluster of brilliant red, tubular flowers on a two- to three-foot, erect, four-sided stem. The broad, lance-shaped leaves are thin and borne in opposite pairs which alternate and thereby do not shade each other. The tubular flowers are about an inch long and the arched upper lip protrudes over the lower three-parted lip. The stamens and pistil extend beyond the petals, so when an insect perches on the lower lip the stamens are pulled down upon it. The anthers rub against the insect, leaving pollen on its body to be carried to the next flower it visits. The tube of the flower is so long that only butterflies, bumblebees, and hummingbirds can reach to the bottom (*See Pollination*).

All of the species belonging to this genus *Monarda* occur either in Mexico or North America. One species, western horsemint, is the only representative of the genus in the far western states. It has yellowish-white flowers. In the eastern states there are many and their flowers are white, yellow, lavender, or purple.

OTTER
River Otter
Other Common Names—None
Scientific Name—*Lutra canadensis*
Family—Mustelidae (weasels, skunks, and allies)
Order—Carnivora
Size—Male: body length, 38 to 55 inches; tail, 12 to 19 inches; weight, 10 to 30 pounds. Females 30 percent smaller
Range—Throughout North America except extreme northern Canada and desert areas of southwestern United States

Habits of the River Otter

Perhaps the most playful four-footed animal in North America is the river otter, *Lutra canadensis.* It lives over much of the United States, from Canada south to Florida and west to the Pacific Coast, along creeks, rivers, brooks, lakes, and even marine coves, estuaries, and about islands. The dense fur of this long-bodied, short-legged animal, is brownish when wet, and often grayish when dry. Litters of young "pups" are one to four (usually two or three), and are born in February to April in the North, earlier in the South. Otters apparently live long in captivity—a female was still birthing litters at seventeen years of age, and another lived at least nineteen years.

The otter has progressed far along the line of development suited for an aquatic life; its streamlined body, short limbs, and webbed feet are adaptations for torpedolike speed in the water. Though the otter has a wide distribution and is found in most countries it was never abundant in any part of its range. Its valuable coat is not only highly prized in the market today but was much coveted by primitive people. Despite the fact that it has been vigorously hunted

The river otter's streamlined body and webbed feet make it an expert swimmer

throughout the ages the otter still maintains much of its former range, and actually exists on suitable watercourses a few miles out of even the largest cities of America. It is an apt fisherman and its den can often be determined by a pile of fish scales on the bank of a stream or lake. It is good tempered and playful at all times.

Though the streams of American farmland country may be a familiar route to an otter, the dark, secretive animal is rarely seen by those who till these lands. A creature of lakes and rivers, it leads its shy, but full existence unknown to the people who own the land. Yet the otter is one of the most interesting of animals, exemplifying the spirit of play—of fun for fun's sake. The mink, the otter's cousin, plays, but a mink's play is solitary.

Otters seek company when they turn to sport. What other wild creatures gather regularly for coasting parties? As woodsmen know, otters like nothing better than to slide, one after another, down a snowy bank into the water of a stream or lake. They tuck their forelegs straight beneath them and go "belly-whopper," then climb back up the bank, like any group of human youngsters, to recapture the flying thrill. In summer they will accept a grassy bank as a substitute slide for snow, and southern otters will slide down slick clay banks. Such is the ebullient spirit of the otter that it does not restrict its fun to coasting, but will also play tag and stage mock battles.

In addition to possessing a highly prized pelt, the otter must contend with the enmity of many fishermen, who regard the otter as a competitor. Yet the analyses of the stomach contents of otters have shown that, even in game-fish waters, an appreciable proportion of the otter's diet consists of forage fishes, crayfishes, and amphibians, and speedy trout are passed up in favor of slower-moving prey. Like other carnivores, the otter eats what it can catch. When times are lean it will include insects and earthworms in its diet.

At intervals one may see an otter's tracks (*see Animal Tracks*) along a stream bank for a few days at a time. These intervals are due to the otter's habit of circling a wide area, a habit caused by the necessity of following its food supply. In winter, as one stream or lake freezes over, the otter must move on till it finds another body of open water, and sometimes it journeys overland between waterways. But recurrently, the tracks and the sweeping paths along the river's edge appear if an otter has made its home nearby. By searching along a riverbank one may discover the otter's wide-mouthed burrow. It is usually cleverly hidden by the grasses topping the bank. The burrow may be 18 inches across at its opening though narrowing a bit as it descends steeply downward. It is usually far too wide for the work of a mink, muskrat or woodchuck. Further investigation may show a definite trail running from the den to the flattened grasses on the bank above.

Otter family life is as rollicking an affair as is their habit of coasting. Both parents enter wholeheartedly into its spirit, though, until the pups are some three months old, the adult female keeps the male parent at a distance. Then, however, the little unit becomes a true family group. There is a great deal of exuberant play. The mother teaches the pups to swim, and the father helps to train them. As the summer wanes, the father goes his own way, but mother and pups are often together when the nip of winter is in the air. —H.S.J.

Sea Otter
Other Common Names—None
Scientific Name—*Enhydra lutris*
Family—Mustelidae (weasels, skunks, and allies)
Order—Carnivora
Size—Male: body length, 40 to 69 inches; tail, 10 to 11 inches; weight, 25 to 75

The sea otter is the only marine mustelid, a group that includes the weasels and skunks

pounds. Females considerably smaller
Range—Pacific Coast from Aleutian Islands to southern California, and south in Old World along Pacific Coast to Kamchatka, Kuril, and Bonin Island

There is one living member of the mustelines that can be termed a marine mammal—the sea otter (the sea mink is now extinct). The fabulous price set on its pelt brought the sea otter to the verge of extinction many years ago. Fortunately, conservation laws were enforced just in time to save a few remnants of this historical race. When the sea otter was first met with along the Pacific Coast of North America it was a friendly trusting creature, coming ashore to breed and sun itself. Today this same otter spends its entire life among the kelp beds offshore; under no circumstances will it trust its priceless hide on shore where lurk the treacherous two-footed predators.

OUZEL (*See under Dipper*)

OVENBIRD

Other Common Names—Teacher, golden-crowned thrush, wood wagtail
Scientific Name—*Seiurus aurocapillus*
Family—Parulidae (wood warblers)
Order—Passeriformes
Size—Length, 5½ to 6½ inches
Range—Breeds from Newfoundland to northwestern Canada, south to eastern North Carolina, northern Georgia, Arkansas, Oklahoma, and Colorado. Winters from southern South Carolina, the Gulf Coast, and south to Colombia and Venezuela

Some birds are heard more often than they are seen. The ovenbird is one of these. It is a voice in the woods, calling *teacher, teacher, teacher, teacher,* repeated rapidly, louder and louder, until the air rings with the vibrant accents. It is not a conspicuous bird in its breeding territory. It is about the size of a sparrow and walks nervously over the dead leaves or along a log. It is olive-brown with a streaked breast, undistinguished except for a noticeable ring around its big, beady eyes and a light orange patch on the top of its head.

Although the ovenbird is much like a thrush, it actually is a warbler. Warblers are usually brightly colored, thin-billed birds, but several, including the ovenbird, depart from the family characters. The ovenbird lives in the leafy shadows of the forest, like a thrush. It has the big eyes of a thrush and acts like a thrush (*See under Warbler*).

The ovenbird, like the red-eyed vireo, ranks near the top of the list of the most abundant birds of the East. And like the vireo, it is unknown to the average man whose knowledge of birds hardly goes beyond the robins, grackles, and starlings in his own yard. There are millions of ovenbirds, but they still do not compare with red-eyed vireos in numbers, because they do not occupy quite as much of the continent, and because they they have larger territories. Each pair of ovenbirds requires three or four acres of

The ovenbird is one of the most common birds in eastern forests

forest territory while a pair of red-eyed vireos requires only an acre or two.

The ovenbird has another song that is not commonly heard. It might be given any hour of the day or night, but is not performed often. Rising above the treetops, it pours out a wild warble and then drops back into the forest shadows. Several of the familiar *teachers* can be heard at the tail end of the song, giving a clue to the singer's identity. The song is most often heard at night when the forest is silent.

The ovenbird received its name from the nest it builds—a domed-over structure with an entrance on one side, like the old-fashioned outdoor ovens that are still used in some parts of Europe. It is built among the brown leaves on the woodland floor and is not easy to find unless the bird flutters from the nest. Sometimes it is covered with dead leaves, but other nests, roofed over with grasses, are hidden in a setting of ferns and small woodland plants.

The cup inside the leafy shelter is lined with grass and hair. The four to five eggs are white with brown spots. The female incubates them for about 12 days. For another 10 days both birds make countless trips in and out among the ferns and over the leaves, bringing in smooth green caterpillars and other insects, including beetles, ants, bugs, and worms.

Some ovenbirds start their migration in August with the other warblers that are traveling in little bands through the woodlands. By late September most of the ovenbirds have gone. A few ovenbirds winter in Florida and some stop on islands along the coast of Louisiana, but most of them reach the tropics and spend the winter from the West Indies and Mexico to northern South America.

—A.B., Jr.

OWL

Owls are among the most cosmopolitan of birds. To locate the range of many species would require a globe of the world. The great gray owl, the snowy owl, boreal owl, and hawk owl inhabit the more northern latitudes of the entire northern hemisphere. Barn owls and long-eared owls are at home in Europe, Asia, and North America. The short-eared owl lives on every continent except Australia. Even the great horned owl and the screech owl, although restricted to the western hemisphere, are widely distributed over both North and Central America.

About the size of a bluebird, the pygmy owl lives in the coniferous forests of western North America

A barn owl approaches its nest in a tree hollow

Barn Owl
Other Common Names—Monkey-faced owl, golden owl
Scientific Name—*Tyto alba*
Family—Tytonidae (barn owls)
Order—Strigiformes
Size—Length, 18 inches
Range—Nearly cosmopolitan. In New World from British Columbia, North Dakota, Michigan, southern Ontario and southern New England south to the West Indies, Central and South America to Tierra del Fuego. In Old World from British Isles, Baltic and southern Russia south through Africa, southeastern Asia to Australia

The barn owl is well suited for its task in life. Its ears, with their remarkable powers, are able to penetrate the darkness and detect the movement of a mouse among the leaves. The large ear openings, placed right beneath the rim of the white facial disks, are sensitive

The barn owl is effective in limiting the number of destructive rodents near farms

to the faintest sound. The bird moves as silently as a shadow, the long, loose feathers deadening any sound it might make. The hooked beak, the strong curved claws—everything about the bird, is perfectly formed for its purpose.

Although the old owls will remain throughout the year in their chosen haunts, there is a regular migration of barn owls in the fall of the year. These are young birds. Occasionally these congregate on their way south in groves of pines or pin oaks where they escape notice.

Barred Owl
Other Common Names—Hoot owl, wood owl
Scientific Name—*Strix varia*
Family—Strigidae (typical owls)
Order—Strigiformes
Size—Length, 20 inches
Range—Northern Canada southward, east of Rocky Mountains through eastern Montana; Wyoming and northeastern Colorado, Texas, Louisiana and Florida to Mexico and Central America

Like all owls, the barred owl is more often heard than seen. Its common call is a series of eight hoots that seem to say, *Who cooks for you, who cooks for you-all.* The last hoot of the second group is long drawn out, and drops in pitch.

This owl is found in swamps and deep woods, although when hunting it may be seen over adjacent open areas. It prefers to roost and nest in hollow trees, but where these are scarce it may use an old nest of a hawk or squirrel. Occasionally it may be heard calling at any time of the day, and on dark days it is active from mid-afternoon on.

The food of the barred owl, like that of most owls, is varied. It includes about everything living in its habitat that is large enough to be worthy of notice, yet small enough to be captured. As this owl has comparatively small and weak talons, it seldom molests large birds or mammals, but lives on mice, insects, fishes, crayfishes, frogs, and small birds. Much of its food is swallowed whole and such indigestible materials as fur, feathers, bones, fish scales, and insect wings are later regurgitated in the form of pellets. The pellets reveal, if studied throughout the year, the barred owl's food habits.

Burrowing Owl
Other Common Names—Billy owl, ground owl
Scientific Name—*Speotyto cunicularia*
Family—Strigidae (typical owls)
Order—Strigiformes
Size—Length, 8½ to 9 inches
Range—Breeds in the prairies of central Florida and in western North America from southern British Columbia to southern Manitoba south to Louisiana and west to the Pacific Coast. Winters in same areas except the burrowing owls that breed north of Kansas migrate southward

The burrowing owl lives in most of the states west of the Mississippi River and in the prairie provinces of Canada. It also occurs in the prairie regions of Florida. Perhaps, in the dim past, burrowing owls lived across the southern part of the United States, but somehow they got separated. The Florida owls, isolated as they are, have become a little different, a little darker. The difference is not apparent, however, unless the two varieties are standing side by side. In one way, they are quite different—the Florida bird digs its own hole, the western one appropriates the abandoned hole of a prairie dog or a badger.

Sometimes several pairs of owls, a dozen, or even more, will form a little colony in a prairie dog town. Each will sit, in broad daylight, on the mound of dirt at the mouth of the hole. When danger nears, they bob their heads, stretch themselves high on their long legs, then bow low. After bowing and scraping, they bow with their backs turned to the approaching danger, not quite sure whether to fly, stay there a minute longer, or rush inside the hole.

Usually six, eight, or even nine white eggs are laid in the chamber at the end of the tunnel. They are nearly round, more so than those of most birds. They hatch into fuzzy, white chicks. A diet of beetles, young gophers, frogs, and crayfishes makes them grow so fast that by the time they are about three weeks old, they can take a look at the world outside. The whole family then sits in the sun at the edge of the hole. When

From mid-afternoon on, the barred owl moves through the dense forest

Burrowing owls prefer abandoned animal burrows for homes but are capable of excavating their own burrows when necessary

At a little over five inches in length, the elf owl is the smallest owl in North America

danger approaches, the young owls rush into the hole first and are followed by the mother. The father flies off to a distant post or knoll where he can watch the intruder.

At dusk and again before dawn, and all night when the moon is bright, the mournful calls of the little burrowing owls can be heard from far and near. When near, the call sounds like the syllables *cook-a-roo,* but farther off suggests a frightened child calling *pa-pa* in a high, anxious voice. —A.B., Jr.

Elf Owl
Other Common Names—Whitney's owl
Scientific Name—*Micrathene whitneyi*
Family—Strigidae (typical owls)
Order—Strigiformes
Size—Length, 5½ inches
Range—Southwestern United States; southeastern California, central Arizona, southwestern New Mexico and southern Texas to Baja California and Mexico

The great gray owl is the largest member of its group in North America

Great Gray Owl
Other Common Names—Spectral owl
Scientific Name—*Strix nebulosa*
Family—Strigidae (typical owls)
Order—Strigiformes
Size—Length, 27 inches
Range—Limit of tree growth from Alaska to northern Ontario, south in Sierra Nevada to central California, northern Idaho, western Montana, Wyoming, and northern Minnesota. In Old World, from Lapland and northern Russia to Siberia and Mongolia

Great Horned Owl
Other Common Names—Virginia horned owl, big hoot owl
Scientific Name—*Bubo virginianus*
Family—Strigidae (typical owls)
Order—Strigiformes
Size—Length, 22 inches
Range—North America from northern limit of tree growth south to the straits of Magellan. Absent in West Indies

This large owl is one of our most powerful birds of prey. It has few, if any equals in its ability to thrive in almost any environment, even in the face of considerable persecution. It is at home in the deepest of forests and swamps, yet it also persists on the very outskirts of some of our largest cities. Its call is a series of deep, monotonous hoots, usually five.

The absurdity of arbitrarily labeling any bird as either harmful or beautiful becomes apparent when one considers a species like the great horned owl. To the careless farmer who lets his chickens roost in the open, it is harmful. However, to make it beneficial to him, the farmer needs only to spend a few dollars on a good chicken house. The owl must then turn for food to the rabbits and woodchucks that are eating the farmer's crops. Except as their activities infringe directly on human interests, wild animals cannot properly be called either harmful or beneficial.

Inherited instincts determine just

An immature great horned owl

Great horned owls from Audubon's Elephant Folio

what foods are acceptable to each species, and among such foods, those that can be obtained with the least effort are the ones that are utilized. Nature seems to provide that the quantity consumed by any animal is never so great as to threaten its future food supply.

Long-eared Owl
Other Common Names—Cat owl, lesser horned owl
Scientific Name—*Asio otus*
Family—Strigidae (typical owls)
Order—Strigiformes
Size—Length, 14½ inches
Range—Southern Alaska and Canada south to Virginia, Arkansas, Oklahoma, Arizona, and Baja California to central Mexico. In Old World from British Isles, western Europe, Siberia, and Japan south to Mediterranean region, Afghanistan, Himalayas, Korea, and Formosa

This species, with its conspicuous ear tufts and striking plumage of black and white and buff, is one of our most beautiful owls. Moreover, its unusual facial disk lends an added charm to its generally attractive appearance. Like the

Although the long-eared owl has a tremendous range, little is known about it because of its nocturnal habits

screech owl, it is strictly nocturnal in its habits, and usually spends its days in thick evergreen woods or in dense swamps.

The long-eared owl eats large numbers of mice and other rodents, seldom catching birds. It preys also upon moles and beetles. In view of these facts, this owl should be spared from all persecution.

The ornithologist A.K. Fisher has reported that, "of 107 stomachs examined, 1 contained a gamebird; 15, other birds; 84, mice; 5, other mammals; 1, insects; and 15 were empty."

Its nest is usually placed in an old hawk's, crow's, or squirrel's nest, and from three to six white eggs are laid. While the female is sitting on the nest, the male is usually close by, either on the edge beside her or on a limb near at hand.

Screech Owl
Other Common Names—Gray owl, little dukelet, shivering owl
Scientific Name—*Otus asio*
Family—Strigidae (typical owls)
Order—Strigiformes
Size—Length, 8 to 10 inches
Range—Breeds throughout the United

Screech owls usually nest in tree hollows or old woodpecker holes. This pair has taken up residence in a telephone pole

States from southern Canada to Florida, Baja California, and Mexico. Winters in breeding areas

The screech owl is the best known of all the owls in North America. It is the only common small owl with ear tufts. These are not really ears but only feather ornamentations. The real ears are little openings in the side of the head, hidden by the feathers.

In the East, screech owls occur in two colors or phases—gray, and brick-red. This has long puzzled naturalists as there seems to be no connection with age, sex, or season. In the West, all screech owls are gray, except in parts of the Northwest where there are some dark brown ones. There is another dif-

The screech owl has a wingspread of 20 to 24 inches

Screech owls from Audubon's Elephant Folio

ference between the screech owls of the East and of the West. Eastern screech owls have a distinctive shivering wail—*who who who who who who who*—that starts high and then trails low. The call of the western screech owls is lower and all on the same pitch—*who—who—who-who-whowhowho*—that accelerates as it progresses.

The screech owl seems to be most vocal before daybreak just as the sky is beginning to lighten. Then its wail rings loud and clear, but by the time the first songbirds awaken, it can be seen hurrying through the trees to its dark roosting hole in some large oak or sycamore.

Sometimes the screech owl nests in the same hole where it has slept all winter, or it might use a deserted woodpecker hole nearby. There are usually four eggs, rarely more than six. Like those of most other owls, the glossy white eggs are nearly round.

The fuzzy young which hatch in about 24 days are blind ar first. Their eyes do not open until they are over two weeks old, and then all they can see is the dim daylight coming through the opening of their dark cavern. White at first, they gradually change to a barred plumage. Their ear tufts are very rudimentary; in fact, these do not develop for several months, even though by midsummer the young resemble their parents in other respects. When they first leave the nest hole at night to sit on a nearby limb, their parents will fly at animals, or even people, walking below. On bright moonlit nights, whole families of screech owls can be seen darting from the high branches of trees.

Screech owls eat moths, grasshoppers, and other large insects, but the major part of their food is made up of mice, frogs, snakes, and other small creatures. There can hardly be a better asset to an orchard than a pair of screech owls; they help control the mice that girdle the younger trees. Although not a general habit, some screech owls eat small birds but, in turn, they must watch out for the larger owls.

Screech owls do not seem to migrate, although they wander somewhat and turn up in the fall in the most unlikely places. By sitting still, they usually escape notice, looking like a bunch of dried leaves, a dead stub, or a piece of bark. —A.B., Jr.

Short-eared Owl
Other Common Names—Marsh owl, prairie owl
Scientific Name—*Asio flammeus*
Family—Strigidae (typical owls)
Order—Strigiformes
Size—Length, 15½ inches
Range—Northern Alaska, Mackenzie, Baffin Island, and central Greenland south through Utah, Colorado, Kansas, Missouri, and Virginia to West Indies and South America. Northern Scandinavia, Russia, and Siberia, south to Mediterranean area, Afghanistan to Caroline and Hawaiian Islands

The short-eared owl differs from most members of its family in being a bird of the open country. It inhabits swamps and low, wet meadows, frequenting both coastal and inland marshes. In these, its favorite haunts, it preys upon mice and shrews, which constitute about 75 percent of its food. It very rarely preys upon birds. In a study in which short-eared owl stomachs were examined, 11 out of 101 stomachs contained birds; 77, mice; 7, other mammals; and 7, insects. Fourteen stomachs were empty.

This owl is not at all shy, and is rarely flushed until almost stepped upon. Its flight is graceful and noiseless. During the winter single individuals are often seen, but now and then small groups or even colonies numbering a hundred or more may be found.

The nest is placed on the ground and is a rude affair of grass and sticks and is lined with fine materials. Occasionally the nest is placed in low

The snowy owl is a wanderer of the arctic tundra. Its white plumage is sometimes barred or spotted with light to dark brown

bushes. From three to five white eggs are laid.

Snowy Owl
Other Common Names —Arctic owl, great white owl
Scientific Name—*Nyctea scandiaca*
Family—Strigidae (typical owls)
Order—Strigiformes
Size—Length, 25 inches
Range—Circumpolar in tundra areas north of the limit of tree growth. South in winter to central Europe, central Asia, and northern United States

The Habits of Owls

Unlike most birds owls have so many characteristics that seem almost human that they have long been given credit for wisdom they do not possess, and even for magical powers. Contributing to this impression are large eyes that look straight out as a human being's do, a facial disk, earlike tufts of feathers, and deep voices. But owls are *predators*. That is, they kill and eat other animals (mostly vertebrates) in order to exist, and because of this they themselves are often killed by man.

Killing of smaller animals by predators is neither cruel nor wasteful. It seldom upsets anything—except perhaps a few people who have not considered the benefits very carefully. The role of predators is a product of the evolution of life itself and is a necessary function in every sizeable community of living things. Indeed, one can hardly understand predation apart from its community role (*See Wildlife: The Wildlife Community*). For years men have tried to unravel these relationships by studying one *raptor* (a combination term for hawks and owls) or its effects on one species at a time. This did little to improve understanding or to relieve prejudices about these birds. But some recent attempts to measure the effect of the total population of prey animals does promise to give new understanding.

Prey-predator interrelationships are very complex, and it will long remain difficult to see the picture as a whole. Much as there is to learn, however, there are already several good rules of thumb to guide one's thinking. These are so important to full understanding that they may be called biological concepts (*See also under Predation*).

Biological Concept No. One—Predators usually take prey in proportion to the ready availability of that prey. This rule holds so well that it may even be said that the numbers of raptors are an indication of the numbers of favorite prey animals. For example, the presence of numerous hawks and owls in an area almost certainly means there are many mice there for rodents are the principal item of diet for most raptors.

Forgetting that rodents are the chief prey for many predators, people often seek to destroy predators because they may occasionally take species considered more desirable by human standards (quail, for example). This "conflict of interest" is best solved by improving living conditions (better food and cover combinations) for the species we want to protect, and not by eliminating the predators, as we have too often done in the past.

When we eliminate the predators we disrupt the natural process by which excessive increases in the populations of mice and other prey species are normally prevented. We are then working against nature instead of with her, and this always proves expensive, sometimes disastrous for us. The point is that healthy natural communities are almost always in reasonably good balance. If one attempts to correct occasional and temporary imbalances by removing important elements of the community—predator control at first seems *so* logical—one soon finds oneself in the predicament of the man who tries to restore balance to a table by shortening first one leg and then another.

Nature has patiently worked out all these problems by maintaining a dynamic balance, that retains community stability despite the fluctuations of the many components of that community. And these arrangements have stood the test of several million years. For example, owls have become specially adapted to work the "night shift" in exerting biological pressure on the numbers of smaller prey animals. They replace the hawks that work by day. Not only do they perform the same role in nature, but owls replace hawks almost species for species and size for size in various habitats.

As just one example, the great horned owl has its counterpart in the red-tailed hawk. This means that there is a marvelous overlapping of functions with a minimum of interference in carrying out an important community service, namely the balancing of small animal numbers within reasonable limits. These small animals also have evolved as parts of the community and their reproductive powers are *adapted* to this predation pressure. When one species in the community, owing perhaps to especially favorable conditions, produces more young than is normal, more predators prey on that species. By the same token, when a prey species is having other troubles and its numbers decline, the predators shift to more common forms. Predators do not like to work any harder than they have to in order to make a living. They take whatever is the easiest. In nature there is seldom time or energy to waste on futile pursuits. Finally, when there is a general decline in prey populations, a parallel decline in predator numbers occurs.

How this system works can be visualized by analyzing a small segment of it.

In the diversified landscape of much of the northern United States where small woodlots and farms and suburban areas are more or less evenly scattered, the fan-tailed *Buteo* hawks, almost all of them habitual mouse eaters, make up about 35 percent of the nesting raptor population (*See Buteo*).

The red-shouldered hawk is usually the commonest of these. Next in abundance is the little screech owl, making up about 20 percent of the clan. Another 35 percent is made up of a varying collection of species, and the final 10 percent—only one out of 10 raptors—is made up of the great horned owl, the tiger of the woods. This bird's size and strength, and its varied diet, make it the most powerful bird in most wooded areas of North America.

The Mathematics of Predation

There are today nearly 400 recognized species of raptors (264 hawks and 134 owls) in the world. In all of them the female is larger and heavier than the male.

For example, female great horned owls weigh about 1,700 grams, males only 1,300. From studies of captive birds, we know that large birds like these must eat daily about 10 percent of their weight in prey during the colder half of the year, only 8 percent in milder months. Smaller raptors like the screech owl, which weighs only about 172 grams (average for both sexes), must eat the equivalent of 25 percent and 17 percent of their weight during these same periods. Why? Because small animals have more surface area relative to body mass than large ones; they therefore lose heat faster and require more food (fuel) to maintain body temperature.

Even so powerful a bird of prey as the great horned owl eats mostly mice, up to 90 percent of its diet in good mouse years, although it can and does sometimes take almost any animal it encounters which is no larger than itself. It takes crows, rabbits, house cats, muskrats, and many others, but seldom in any numbers because, again, mice are normally so numerous that they are an easier means of satisfying the food energy requirements of this owl.

One can compute the food requirements of a pair of great horned owls as nearly 50,000 grams of meat per bird per year. Because it is a woods dweller, this owl feeds mostly on the white-footed mouse (*Peromyscus*). About 75 percent of its mouse diet is of this woodland species, the other 25 percent consisting of field mice (*Microtus* and its relatives). Since these two mice weigh 14 and 34 grams, respectively, a little more arithmetic shows that one such

The regurgitation of pellets containing indigestible matter such as bones, feathers, and fur is habitual with all owls and serves as a convenient means of identifying their diets

owl, if 90 percent of its diet were mice, would eat over 2,750 mice per year; the pair of them would eat some 5,500 mice; and given two young for half a year, a family would consume some 8,250 mice.

But it should be remembered that these great horned owls are only 10 percent of the raptor population. Several other hawk and owl species are better mousers than the great horned owl. Even so, all hawks and owls in a region, working day and night at the task of controlling the mouse hordes, take less than one-third of the total mouse population in most years, leaving food for and work to be done by foxes, weasels, and other predators. This fact provides an inkling to the important role these raptors and the other predators play in maintaining balance within natural communities.

Man has been prejudiced about predators in general, and hawks and owls in particular, because he has jumped to the conclusion that predation is a subtraction process—the "one quail for the fox is one less for the hunter" sort of reasoning. It has taken a long time to learn enough about the basic function of predation to ask the right questions about it. Once aware of these facts, one no longer asks, "What does it eat?" but rather, "What effect do these food habits have on the *population* of the prey?" The 8, 250 mice computed as the animal toll of a single owl family (above) means little of itself. One needs to know what the total mouse population was during that year before the controllng effect of this predation can begin to be measured. The same rule would apply if the owls were eating birds instead of mice.

Once predation is accepted as an important biological process, and is seen as part of a normal community's functioning, it can be used as a wildlife management tool: (1) Predation will help keep populations of prey healthy by whittling them down to size, and, it turns out, this will be the best size not only for the community but for their own good. Herein lies Biological Concept No. Two. It has been found, and only recently, that the individuals, in a population of small mammals are healthiest when their population is about half its potential. It may soon be discovered that this is a characteristic of all populations.

Another management use of predation, (2), is the ability to change or redistribute survival pressure on certain prey animals simply by changing the environment (mostly cover conditions) in such a way as to expose or protect them so that they may either increase or decrease.

A final Biological Concept, No. Three, is based on the recent conclusion of ecologist Charles Elton, that the most stable environments—perhaps the only stable environments—are those with a diversified abundance of living things, both plant and animal.

For example, insect outbreaks are almost unheard of in highly diversified tropical forests. There are more insect species there than in simpler temperate zone environments, so many perhaps that they buffer one another, and no one species gets out of hand. In the oversimplified environments of modern agriculture, however, insect pests seem to become progressively more difficult to control, despite, or perhaps because of the increasing use of insecticides that kill all but a few resistant species. A naive faith in man's ability to "master" nature is eliminating insect predators which help keep the pest species in check, and he must now try to do the whole "balancing" job himself. It is turning out to be impossible. Indeed, modern agricultural-production boosters very much resemble the man with a saw and an unsteady table, already mentioned.

This is an important discovery, one which has significance for all life, including humans. No one who has progressed to this third biological concept need ever again ask, "What good is it?"

It is now known that the justification for any living thing is not economic or aesthetic—though it may be these, too—but biological. Any organism which has survived several million years of evolution is likely to be an important cog in the intricate system of checks and balances that keeps the face of the earth productive. Owls, like hawks, have the added advantage of being particularly fascinating expressions of Nature's time-tested processes, as man is, too.

Some Adaptive Characteristics of Owls

Reproduction—Owls begin incubating their eggs as soon as the first one is laid. Most other birds wait until the clutch is almost complete. This habit results in progressive hatching of the eggs and means that young owls in a nest may vary in age by several days, at times being as much as a week apart. Since all young birds grow rapidly, this leads to great size differences among the young in the nest. The big early chicks demand, and get, most of the food and the late comers cannot possibly compete on an equal basis.

This habit is also found in hawks, but in very few other species, and is apparently one of nature's mechanisms for adjusting the numbers of predators to the available food supply. When prey species are abundant, owls find it not too difficult to bring up a full clutch of their own; even the runts get fed then because the larger nestlings are at last satisfied. In years of low prey numbers, however, only the largest nestling may get enough to eat. His nestmates starve in such years because owls, like other birds, feed their young by reacting to the demands of the most aggressive, clamorous, and demanding nestling. They cannot keep track of which was or was not fed last time.

Pellets—Owls swallow small prey animals like mice at one gulp—fur, bones, and all. The indigestible fur and bones are rolled into a pellet in the stomach and regurgitated, or cast up, a few hours after feeding. These bones, sometimes entire mouse skulls, and fur are thus good clues to the owl's last meal. Although owl pellets have often provided the first clue to the presence of unexpected small mammals in an area, scientists have learned not to place too much dependence on pellet studies, because it is now known that the food habits of individual owls are only part of the overall predation story. Hawks, too, cast pellets in the same way, and so do shrikes, since their food habits are similar, though shrike pellets are much smaller.

Sight and Hearing—Among the specialized adaptations owls have to help them hunt for a living are their remarkable eyes and ears. The eyes are very large and capable of rapid and very sharp focusing at various distances (this is called accommodation; its loss forces older people to use glasses for reading). Equally important, the eyes are directed forward and since their fields of view overlap greatly, they provide excellent binocular vision, with good depth perception. The eyes, however, are immovably fixed in bony sockets, and to see to the side owls must turn the head toward the object. Extra neck vertebrae provide such great flexibility that owls can turn the head through an arc of 270 degrees. Man and hawks, though they too have binocular vision, can rotate the head only 180 degrees. (*See under Bird*).

This neck twisting sometimes involves very rapid and jerky head movements, and to protect the eyes during such movements owls are provided with a third eyelid called the nictitating membrane. This folds against the inside of the eye and comes out and across the eyeball like a windshield wiper. It also provides protection when the owl flies through foliage, but this is probably a secondary function.

Though owls have an amazing ability to contract or expand the size of the pupil of the eye, this too is an adapta-

Contrary to popular belief, owls can see well in daylight because of their ability to contract and expand the size of the pupil aperture

tion and it is not true, as so many believe, that owls cannot see well in bright sunlight. The snowy owl and the hawk owl of the North are both daytime hunters; it is true, however, that most owls are crepuscular (active at dusk) or nocturnal (at night).

Besides their exceptional vision, owls also have exceptionally keen hearing. Their ears are directed forward (they lie under the facial disc) and are much larger than those of any other group of birds. Amazing, too, is the fact that owls have asymmetrical ears, one with the central fold of the external ear directed downward, the other upward. This enables them to locate most sounds with remarkable exactitude. The combination of exceptional vision and hearing adds up to formidable detection equipment when the owl goes hunting. But nature keeps things in balance. It is thought, for example, that the high-pitched *eeee* alarm notes of small birds are an adaptation to foil predators. Though apparently capable of hearing these warning notes, hawks and owls have difficulty locating such sounds. But the most amazing skill of owls is their ability to locate and actually catch such prey as mice by hearing alone. Laboratory experiments in complete darkness have recently proved that the barn owl can do this rather easily. —R.C.C.

Recommended Reading

The 'Big Boss' of the Woods—Paul L. Errington. **Audubon Magazine,** May-June 1954.
A Closer Look at the Killers—Paul L. Errington. An **Audubon Magazine** reprint.
Hawks, Owls and Wildlife—John J. Craighead and Frank C. Craighead, Jr. Stackpole Company, Harrisburg, Pennsylvania.
Owls—Herbert S. Zim. William Morrow & Company, New York.

OWL'S CLOVER

Common Owl's Clover
Other Common Names—Escobita
Scientific Name—*Orthocarpus purpurascens*
Family—Scrophulariaceae (figwort family)

Owl's clover

Range—Great Valley of California, Coast Ranges from southern Mendocino County to Baja California
Habitat—Open fields, valleys, foothills.
Time of Blooming—March to May

If one looks closely at this reddish-purple flower head he may see small cream-colored owls. These are really tiny cream-colored flowers—like fat little pitchers with lids. Crimson dots on the lids make the eyes. The common name is owl's clover. The magenta-colored heads look much like Indian paintbrush, which is scarlet. One relative is called escobita, which means *little broom.* Another is called cream sacs and still another is called Johnny-nip. These plants grow very close together and make great patches of solid color in the spring.

OX (*See Musk-ox*)

OYSTER

American oyster
Other Common Names—Eastern oyster, Virginia oyster
Scientific Name—*Ostrea virginica*
Family—Ostreidae (oysters)
Order—Prionodesmacea
Size—Length, 4 to 12 inches
Range—Gulf of St. Lawrence to Gulf of Mexico; transplanted to some locations on Pacific Coast

Oysters are bivalves with unequal shells. The left shell is larger than the right and is cemented to a fixed object. The right shell is hinged on the left one, opened by an elastic ligament, and closed by a large adductor muscle. The foot muscle, the organ of locomotion for the mobile bivalves, is poorly developed in this sedentary family.

Microscopic organisms, both animal and vegetable, are consumed by oysters. The gills create currents of water inside the shells, drawing food-filled water over the mouthparts and expelling wastes.

Oyster

One female oyster can lay as many as 60 million eggs at one time, usually in the early summer. Fertilization occurs in the water and the larvae are tiny, at first top-shaped, but later resembling the parents, soon sinking to the bottom. If they chance on a firm foundation, preferably rock or shell, they become adults in about three years.

Where conditions are favorable, tremendous reefs, or beds, of oysters occur. Their natural enemies are numerous and include some species of fishes that crush young oysters, as well as oyster drills and other snails that rasp their limy shells to obtain the soft meat within. Starfishes pull the valves apart and feed on the oyster's soft body.

There are about 100 species of oysters throughout the world. Two species along the Atlantic Coast, the horse oyster of North Carolina waters south to Florida and the coon oyster of Florida and the West Indies, are not considered to be edible. The Olympia oyster of the Pacific Coast rarely exceeds three inches in length. The Japanese oyster and several European species support large oyster fisheries in their respective regions. In economic terms, oysters are the second most important marine crop, surpassed in value only by the herring fishery of the north Atlantic. (*See also Bivalve*) —G.B.S.

OYSTERCATCHER

American Oystercatcher

Other Common Names—Mantled oystercatcher, sea crow

Scientific Name—*Haematopus palliatus*

Family—Haematopodidae (oystercatchers)

Order—Charadriiformes

Size—Length, 19 inches

Range—Nests locally on the Gulf Coast in Texas and Louisiana (east of the Mississippi delta), formerly in Alabama, and western Florida where it is now rare. Also along Atlantic Coast from Long Island, New York, and New Jersey south to Georgia and formerly eastern Florida

Habits of the American Oystercatcher

American oystercatchers fly more like ducks, the white of their underparts, lower backs, and primaries flashing in the sun. When they settle on the beach they stand in the open, their color patterns showing strongly against the glittering background of sand and sea. Their heads, necks, and upper breasts are black, with a faint, bluish-green luster. Using binoculars to bring them closer, one will note that their eyes are orange-yellow, circled with red lids, and that their short legs are between lead and flesh color.

Their beaks are very striking, about four inches long, broad, flattened laterally like knives, and bright red. Oystercatchers, particularly the big females, measure 19 inches long, with a wingspread of 3 feet. Of all American shorebirds, only the long-billed curlew is larger and has longer wings.

After preening a moment they run a few steps, rather more nimbly than one would expect from such bulky birds. Presently, one of them may plunge its bill into the wet sand as if groping for something, and twitch out a small clam. In similar fashion, they seize bloodworms, shrimps, crayfishes, and sand fleas—the big, translucent kind.

Mollusks are their favorite food, although they also like sea urchins, crabs,

Young American oystercatchers hatch on the upper beach

and small starfishes. Their stout beaks make mincemeat of all such creatures, but are equal to much harder work. They hammer barnacles off shoreside rocks, and readily smash open razor clams and other shellfishes.

Raccoon-oysters are their standby. These grow together in sharp-edged clusters, extremely hard to tear apart, and abound in southern creeks, inlets, and lagoons. Oystercatchers deftly thrust their bills between the edges of the valves, cut the adductor muscles, and devour these mollusks by the dozen—so many, it is said, that their flesh tastes somewhat like them.

It is difficult to open an oyster, a quahog, or even a sizeable mussel without the proper implement. One must learn to locate the precise spot near the hinge before he can force the bivalve asunder even with a regular oyster knife (*See Bivalve*). An oystercatcher has a better and a natural tool in its tough vermilion mandibles. Oysters of every kind are stubborn, close-lipped mollusks but they are helpless before an oystercatcher.

Nevertheless, S. Bayliss S. Smith, a British ornithologist who has studied European oystercatchers and photographed them for years, declares that these birds greatly prefer mussels because they are easier to split open. C. J. Maynard, an early American ornithologist, quoted by A. H. Howell in *Florida Bird Life,* long ago reported watching flocks "alight among the oysters and when the bivalves gaped open, as is their habit when the water first leaves them, the birds would thrust in the point of their hard, flat bills, divide the ligament with which the shells are fastened together, then, having the helpless inhabitant at their mercy, would at once devour it." He concluded, "They were not long in making a meal, for scientific specimens which I shot after they had been feeding a short time were so crammed that by simply holding a bird by the legs and shaking it gently the oysters would fall from its mouth."

John James Audubon also reported watching oystercatchers "seize the bodies of gaping oysters on, what are called in the southern states and Florida, 'racoon-oyster beds,' smash a 'razor-handle' against the sand, and suck sea urchins." He likewise writes of seeing an oystercatcher "knock off limpets on the coast of Labrador, using its weapon sideways and insinuating it between the rock and the shell like a chisel."

In the days of Audubon and Alexander Wilson, a pioneering Scottish-American ornithologist, these birds were conspicuous as far north as Labrador and Nova Scotia. Their range includes both coasts of North America, Mexico, Central America, the West Indies, and the shores of South America to southern Chile and Argentina.

On the Atlantic Coast they have been rare north of the Virginia capes, although they are occasionally reported from Long Island and various points in New England. Mrs. C.M. Porter of Center Moriches, Long Island, reported a nesting record there in the summer of 1960, the first for New York State in 100 years.

Oystercatchers were never gunned to any extent. Wild and wary, they seldom assemble in flocks, and they shun decoys. It is almost impossible to stalk one on the open shores of the small islets that it frequents, and who would ever take the trouble, even if it were still considered a gamebird?

Oystercatchers breed locally throughout their range. They lay their eggs, two or three in a set, on mounds between the ocean shore and the first low dune inland. Sometimes they decorate their roomy, bowl-shaped nests with bits of clam shells or scallops. In England and the Hebrides, sets of the European bird's eggs were deposited in depressions prettily lined with grasses whirled into a circle.

The eggs are large, heavily spotted, ovate in contour, and are very hand-

An oystercatcher incubates its three eggs in a shallow depression on the upper beach

some. The base color varies from drab to white, but their protective pattern makes it a bit difficult to see them on the pebbly shore.

The front toes of these birds are basally webbed and they swim and dive well. When they want a bath or a drink they generally fly inland to the nearest fresh water, where they paddle and splash themselves vigorously. Unlike willets, oystercatchers do not betray the whereabouts of their nests by their cries or their actions. They flush and fly far away from any intruder and do not circle back as do so many plovers.

Oystercatchers are birds of the seacoast, and almost never stray from the coastal islands, lagoons, and inlets. They are always a delight to the eye. Fast on the wing and fast on their feet, and wearing striking and picturesque color patterns, they add immensely to the attractiveness of North American barrier islands and lagoons. —H.M.H.

The black oystercatcher lives on the Pacific Coast. It seems to prefer rocky, surf-battered shores and islands, where it feeds on shellfishes, crabs, and squids. The plumage is black, with no white markings. The bill is bright red, and the legs are very pale grayish-pink.

On the lower California coast, an oystercatcher showing white on the wings and the belly is Frazar's oystercatcher, subspecies of the American oystercatcher of the East. This species is also found on the west coast of Central America, and stragglers occasionally reach California. —G.B.S.

P

PADRE ISLAND NATIONAL SEASHORE
Location—The coast of Texas
Size—47,000 acres
Mammals—Muskrats, raccoons
Birdlife—Pelicans, egrets, herons, plovers, skimmers, gulls, terns
Plants—Sea oats, crotons, morning glory

Padre Island National Seashore stretches along the Gulf of Mexico for 80 miles. Most of it is beach and sand dunes, with an occasional freshwater pond. The salt marshes behind the barrier island support one of the most important wintering waterfowl concentrations in the United States. The island is accessible by toll causeways at either end.
Accomodations—In nearby towns
Headquarters—For information write National Park Service, Washington D.C.

PAINTBRUSH
Other Common Names—Dark-lipped annual Indian paintbrush
Scientific Name—*Castilleja spiralis*
Family— Scrophulariaceae (figwort family)
Range — Central California from Lake and Napa counties to Tuolumne County
Habitat—Moist soil along streams—Upper Sonoran Zone
Time of Blooming—June to September

This shows the gay scarlet head of the Indian paintbrush. It looks as if it had been dipped in a cup of color. The plants are a foot or more high, growing in canyons. Sometimes these plants are found growing on the roots of nearby shrubs. This is what we call a parasite—or one that does not earn its own living. The Indian paintbrush does not always do this, for it has a root system of its own. There are other Castillejas that have flowers of yellow, green, and rose color. A very fine red one grows at 11,000 feet elevation—over 2 miles above sea level.

Paintbrush

PAIR-BOND (*See under Bird*)

PALM
The family Palmaceae, the single family in the order Palmales, is almost wholly tropical in distribution. It is one of the largest plant families, with

several thousand species, many of which are not yet taxonomically understood. Palms are monocotyledons, and are one of the very few families in that subclass that have woody tissue and that grow to tree height (*See Monocotyledon*).

Only a few species of palms are native to North America north of Mexico; however, several hundred have been introduced as ornamentals from the tropics of the world. Most of the tropical palms are sensitive to cold and are grown successfully only in southern Florida and southern California. Two specimens of windmill palm, *Trachycarpus fortunei*, from China and Japan, grow in Victoria and British Columbia, and the butia palm, *Butia capitata*, of Brazil is hardy in South Carolina.

Most widespread of the native palms is common palmetto, *Sabel palmetto*. It occurs throughout the West Indies, and as far north as North Carolina. It sometimes attains a height of 80 feet.

Scrub, or dwarf, palmettos, of several different species, grow in a wide variety of habitats from North Carolina south. The plants are trunkless, with both leaves and seed spikes arising from the ground. Each frond is stiff, flattened, and divided radially—a characteristic of the palmettos as opposed to the featherlike division of palm fronds. One species of scrub palmetto, has a recumbent, twisted rootstock, and the fronds produce threadlike filaments along the edges. A palmetto with teeth along the stem it is usually called saw palmetto, *Serenoa repens*.

Two species of thatch palm (*Thrinax*) grow in extreme southern Florida, in the Florida Keys, and in the West Indies. They occasionally reach 30 feet in height, but usually average about 8 feet. The leaves are circular, deeply divided, and about three feet in diameter. A similar and smaller tree, the silver palm (*Coccothrinax*) has finely divided fronds that are silvery on the underside.

The Florida Everglades is the home of the saw cabbage palm (*Paurotis*) another species with radially divided fronds. It grows to 40 feet in height with its roots in fresh water, and always in clumps.

The needle palm, or porcupine palm (*Rhapidophyllum*) is a shrubby species with a reclining trunk, rarely erect, with sharp black spines on the stem. It is densely leaved, and grows in clumps. It occurs naturally from Mississippi through Florida to South Carolina.

The buccaneer palm, hog palm, or Sargent cherry palm (*Pseudophoenix*) once native to a few islands off the Florida coast, no longer occurs in the wild state. It resembles the royal palm, with more sturdy fronds, but seldom reaches 20 feet.

The Floridian royal palm, *Roystonea elata*, is native to a few isolated areas in the southern part of the peninsula. It is noted for its erect, symmetrical, light gray trunk, its secondary column of green frond sheaths, and its gracefully arching fronds. Both it and the Cuban royal palm, *R. regia*, are widely planted in southern Florida.

The Washingtonia palm, *Washingtonia filifera*, found only in a few oases in the Mohave Desert, is used as a street tree in California, Louisiana, and Florida. The straight trunk is often cloaked in a mat of old leaves. The stems of the fronds are armed with recurving thorns.

The ornamental and useful coconut palm, *Cocos nucifera*, with its gracefully leaning trunk and crown of feathery fronds, is now believed to have originated in the East Indies, although the date of its arrival in the New World is unknown. It is now naturalized in southern Florida, and is a popular ornamental in extreme coastal southern California.

During the 16th and 17th centuries, the date palm, *Phoenix dactylifera*, and other species were introduced by Spanish priests into Florida and California. These trees sometimes reach heights of 100 feet. Today, dates are raised commercially in the Coachella Valley in southern California. —G.B.S.

Coconut palm

Coconut Palm
Other Common Names—None
Scientific Name—*Cocos nucifera*
Family—Palmaceae (palm family)
Range—Almost worldwide in the tropics. It grows well in southern Florida and the Florida Keys. Probably native to southern Asia or Polynesia
Habitat—Tropical strands and low plains in areas along shores. Characteristically along Pacific beaches and and lagoons
Leaves—Pinnate, the narrow leaflets growing out from a central vein 12 to 18 feet long and hanging down as much as 3 feet on either side
Bark—A fairly smooth, ribbed gray surface above the swollen base, ringed with the slit-shaped scars of the cast-off leaves
Flowers—In large, many-branched sprays from the growth area at the base of the leaves
Fruit—Clusters of very large nuts, 6 to 8 inches in diameter, 10 to 12 inches long. The smooth, hard outer husk composed of tough, coarse fibers surrounds an even harder nut. It is the white flesh lining this inner shell and the liquid in it that are called coconut "meat" and "milk"

These palms have probably appeared in more travelogues, magazines, and movies of Pacific Island areas than any other tree. Allied military forces visiting the coral atolls of this region often found continuous forests of coconut palms; and in the Hawaiian Islands they grow abundantly on many sea-level margins surrounding the towering volcanic mountains.

Many people do not realize how extensively the coconut palms have established themselves along the beaches of the lower Florida peninsula, in some cases introduced as windbreaks and to hold the sandy shore against the effects of storms. They also spring up quite spontaneously through natural propagation. The giant nuts, hollow inside and surrounded by a very tough, porous mass of fibers and a second, hard outer shell, are the largest nuts or plant seeds in the world. They are bouyant and hence when falling or rolling into the water during high tides are carried off to new locations where, when permanently stranded, they take root.

The vitality and reproductive successes of coconut palms have helped rate it as the most useful of trees to both primitive and civilized peoples, producing an astonishing variety of substances that can provide food, drink, clothing, shelter, hats, baskets, instruments, wharf pilings, and various handcraft items for trade. A whole coconut economy could be described, affecting a surprising variety of peoples throughout the world.

Strange that a tree with such classic decorative appearance and such serious importance to large segments of the world's human population should be somewhat comically named after the three root-exit spots on the end of the husked nut—spots that make it resemble a monkey's face, hence the Portuguese word for monkey, *cocos*. —M.H.B.

Common Palmetto
Other Common Names—Cabbage tree, cabbage palm, sabel palm
Scientific Name— *Sabel palmetto*
Family—Palmaceae (palm family)
Range—Coastal North and South Carolina, through Florida westward to St. Andrews Bay, Florida. Also to the West Indies
Habitat—In lowland areas and coastal dunes
Leaves—Yellow-green fans five to six feet long and about seven feet wide, with an elongated central vein that causes the end to curve downward in characteristic fashion
Bark—Yellowish-gray, with rough, shallow ribbing when the old leaf stems are dropped
Flowers—Large, many-branched sprays

Common palmettos (foreground); and royal palms

of small, yellow flowers, springing from the center of the foliage
Fruit— Small black berries growing in sprays

Palms are so intimately associated with really tropical places that the traveler progressing down the eastern seaboard near the shore may be surprised to see them there. The first palm one sees going southward is the undergrowth of scrub palmetto in shore regions of the Carolina lowlands, but a bit farther down, the cabbage palm appears. The foliage of the young trees pushing up through chest-high vegetation may not look much different from the scrub species at the first glance, but a second look will reveal the much larger leaves, or fronds, with a long central vein.

These young trees grow quite rapidly, first developing a full-breadth crown and then growing upwards until they reach considerable height. This is rather different from most trees that grow upward first and then rather uniformly in all directions.

The palm tree's growth is this way because its structure is different, all the living tissue being in a column up the center with the leaves forming and emerging at the top. The trunk is merely a tough cortex for support and protection and is almost immune to more than superficial damage from fire. The great central "bud" at the top of the trunk can be boiled and eaten, hence the name cabbage palm is locally substituted for the common palmetto. Wharf pilings are sometimes made from the trunks and whisk brooms from the dry stems; and the Indians of the Southeast made a sort of cloth and other items from the fibers.

Some of the common palmettos retain the "skirts" of dead fronds or at least the broken stems, but others shed them and their trunks rise straight and narrow to the spherical mass of green foliage. The sight of their characteristic shapes punctuating the skyline of savannahs and river plains is hardly less tropical in appearance than some equatorial landscapes. It is interesting to note that the northern limits of the range of several cold-blooded creatures (alligator, gopher tortoise, diamondback rattler, the gopher snake, *Drymarchon*, and certain frogs) approximates that of the common palmettos. —M.H.B.

Washingtonia Palm
Other Common Names—Desert palm, fan palm
Scientific Name—*Washingtonia filifera*
Family—Palmaceae (palms)
Range—Desert regions (particularly canyons) of southern California and Baja California, now widely cultivated in California and Florida
Habitat—Semidesert areas
Leaves—Big fans about five feet across, more nearly circular than those of the cabbage palm, with the 40 to 70 leaflets divided only about two-thirds of the way to their base. The leaflets tend to split and droop over at the end, and often have threadlike fibers curling from the margin
Bark—A dark gray; smooth or with shallow ridges where the leaves have been shed naturally
Flowers—Great sprays of tiny blossoms in late May or June
Fruit—Small black berries

Washingtonia is a genus of stout fan palms, several of which are used as ornamentals in parks and gardens in many parts of the world. This particular species grows wild in semidesert areas in California, a handsome tree under which one would expect to see some tropical forms of wildlife. The stiff, round fans, fringed with hairlike fibers and their rather thick stems armed with stout, recurved hooks are easy marks of identification. Like the cabbage palm and others it may or may not retain a mass of dead leaves on its trunk.

Seventy-five feet represents about the maximum height of these trees; 50 feet with a 2-foot-thick trunk would be nearer

Washingtonia palm

average size. Those most often seen around private and hotel grounds, however, are young trees scarcely more than 10 or 15 feet high. The city of New Orleans and various places in Florida have their share of planted Washingtonia palms and they have been grown in warmer parts of Europe with success. The group is named after George Washington, although whether he had seen the trees is a matter of question. —M.H.B.

PALO VERDE

Other Common Names—Blue palo verde, green-barked acacia
Scientific Name—*Cercidium floridum*
Family—Leguminosae (pulse family)
Range—Deserts of Arizona and southern California. (Other shrublike species occur in southern Texas and Mexico)
Habitat—Arid Southwest, mostly on the edges of dry washes
Leaves—Compound sprays only one inch long, with two or three pairs of tiny leaflets
Bark—Smooth green on twigs, corrugated on trunk and larger branches; may be brownish below
Flowers—Bright yellow sprays of three-fourths of an inch, five-petaled blossoms with red-brown anthers
Fruit—Flat beans two to four inches long, ripening in July

Palo verde

Desert plants solve the problems of drying heat and lack of water in several different ways. One of these is represented by such plants as the acacias called palo verde which prevent loss of precious water by shedding their leaves, thus greatly lessening evaporation. In this stripped condition the life processes are carried on at a reduced rate, using what little moisture is available and manufacturing food from the green chlorophyll in the twigs.

With the arrival of the spring rains all the suppressed energies of the palo verde burst into blossom and new leaves. Gradually, as the rains lessen and the heat increases, the leaves are shed and the palo verde again becomes the "green stick" bush of the desert. The only evident sign of life is its green color. The dry pods containing beans, which are eaten by birds, rodents, and other animals, are fully developed by midsummer.

Because palo verde never grows to much more than 20 feet in height with a trunk well under a foot in diameter it has no rating as a source of lumber, but it probably has many local uses, including those of fencing and fuel.

In the early days of the southwestern settlements, when irrigation and deep wells were unheard of, a clump of palo verde might be the only green thing besides cactus to be seen for many miles—a welcome relief to the eye and, perhaps, a hopeful sign of water. Palo verde is the state tree of Arizona.

—M.H.B.

PARASITE

Biologists define a parasite as an animal or plant that depends upon some other animal or plant for food; also (quite often among animal parasites), for shelter and for a place to mate and to lay its eggs. The animal or plant that is parasitized is called the *host,* and is usually, if not always, larger than the parasite.

The parasite, to be successful, or self-perpetuating, must not kill its host, otherwise it would also destroy itself. Consequently, most parasites are essentially nonpathogenic, and may cause disease in the host only under exceptional circumstances.

In nature there are many, varied types of parasitism. Certain animal parasites are called *obligate,* or *permanent,* parasites. For example, protozoan animals that live in the bloodstream of birds and mammals and cause malaria are compulsorily parasitic all their lives. These and tapeworms, for example, that live inside the bird or mammal are not only permanent parasites, but are called *endoparasites* because they live within the body of their hosts. Feather lice (another parasite that is always dependent on the bird host and cannot live apart from it) are called *ectoparasites* because they live outside the body of the bird host.

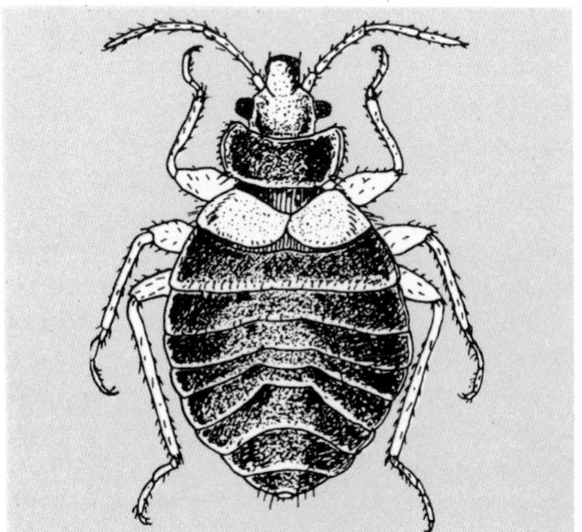

The Mexican chicken bug is a parasite of owls and California condors

Parasites that can spend long periods of time away from their hosts are called *periodical parasites.* Examples are ticks and bedbugs (ectoparasites) that gorge themselves on the blood of certain bird hosts, then drop off into the birds' nests, or nearby, to hide and digest their meals, or to lay their eggs.

One of the most interesting forms of parasitism is called *brood parasitism,* wherein a bird lays its eggs in the nest of another bird species, and the victimized bird host hatches the young and raises them as though they were its own (*See Cowbird*). —J.K.T.

Recommended Reading

Fleas, Flukes, and Cuckoos—Miriam Rothschild and Theresa Clay. The Macmillan Company, New York.

Some Insect Parasites of Birds

The lives of most wild birds are affected by insects. Not all birds are known as insect-eaters, yet possibly every kind of bird is the unwilling host to one or more kinds of bloodsucking arthropods (*See Arthropod*). Such creatures as lice, mites, fleas, and bedbugs live on domestic as well as on wild fowl. A given species of insect may or may not be found on both wild and domestic birds. For example, the common sticktight flea, *Echidnophaga gallinacea,* has been taken from many wild fowl as well as from ordinary poultry.

On the other hand, certain types of lice usually found on wild birds are seldom if ever taken from poultry. Some insects are *host specific* for a special bird; for example, one kind of bedbug may be found only on white-throated swifts, and another kind only on chimney swifts.

In 1947 a scientist in the western United States reported for the first time the discovery of the Mexican chicken bug, *Haematopinus inodorus* (previously found only on domestic poultry), in the nests of two wild North American birds, the California condor and the great horned owl. This prompted a further investigation of this small brown bug, common in poultry houses of the southwestern United States and in Mexico. A small group of scientists, eager to know more about this little-known insect, traveled to some sandy-clay cliffs along the Santa Ana River near Corona, California, not far from an area where the Mexican chicken bug had first been reported in the nests of great horned owls. There, in the abandoned nests of barn owls in caves of the cliff, they found hundreds of the Mexican chicken bug scattered on the ground.

The large numbers of the Mexican chicken bug the scientists found in the owls' nests was astounding. From a single barn owl's nest they took 1,425 specimens; from another 1,778. The bugs were not only in the nest itself, but on the face of the cliff around the nest opening where they hid in cracks and crevices, laid their eggs, shed their outgrown skins, and carried on other phases of their interesting life cycle.

The life history of the Mexican chicken bug was later studied in the laboratory where other interesting facts about it were discovered. Instead of having the usual five stages between egg and adult that nearly all other true bugs of the order Hemiptera have, the Mexican chicken bug has but four. This insect seems to prefer light. The bedbug associated with humans shuns light and feeds only in darkness or subdued light.

Other Bedbug Parasites of Birds

The Mexican chicken bug is not the only member of the bedbug family found in the nests of wild birds. The nest of cliff swallows are often teeming with swallow bedbugs. How these insects can last through the winter without blood food until the following cliff-swallow season is not positively known. However, as one professor at the University of California remarked, "When the swallows come back to Capistrano, the bedbugs will be there waiting for them." It is possible that the insects feed on an occasional avian transient.

Collecting swallow bedbugs is generally a fairly simple matter. The abandoned nests are not too difficult to find, nor are they very hard to reach. Since this species of bedbug is so widely distributed geographically it is almost a sure thing to find them infesting a recently occupied nest.

Such ease in collecting is not the case when one is after the bug, *Synxenoderus comosus,* found in nests of the elusive white-throated swifts. These fast-flying birds seem to prefer the most inaccessible nesting sites imaginable. Practically nothing is known of the life habits of the bedbug that lives in the nests of the white-throated swift, nor of its effects on its bird host. W.C. Hanna, a noted California ornithologist, was the first scientist to collect specimens of this insect from the nests of white-throated swifts. They usually build their nests deep in the cracks of almost unscalable rocks or high up under a jutting shelf of stone.

Other wild birds in North America have bedbug problems, too. Another species of bug, *Hesperocimex coloradensis,* has been reported from Mexico on the gray-breasted martin and other swallows. *Cimexopsis nyctalis,* yet another member of the bedbug family, may be found on the chimney swift in the eastern and central United States. Very little is known about these insects. Undoubtedly, if they were collected more frequently their life histories and the role they play in the ecology of their avian hosts would be studied and better understood.

The information now known about bedbugs that parasitize birds is indeed meager when compared with the knowledge yet to be gained by diligent study. Entomologists are often limited in their field of operations and may not have the opportunity to examine birds' nests from as large an area as they would like.

Cliff swallow nests often teem with bedbugs

Modern science can no longer depend on the efforts of individual men working alone; achievement is based on the efforts of many men from many professions working together. Professional and amateur ornithologists can help the entomologists by collecting insects they find on birds or in their nests. Entomologists can help those interested in birds by studying the parasites found on birds, and the role of diseases sometimes transmitted from bird to bird by the parasites. —R.D.L.

PARASITISM (*See under Bee: The Parasitic Bumblebees; and under Insect: Insect Values*)

PARTHENOGENESIS (*See Insect: Insect Predators*)

PARTRIDGE

Chukar

Other Common Names—Rock partridge
Scientific Name—*Alectoris graeca*
Family—Phasianidae (Quails, pheasant, and peacocks)
Order—Galliformes
Size—Length, 13 inches
Range—Southeastern Europe, Asia; introduced into dry country between the Rockies and the Sierras

The light gray color of the chukar partridge is strongly contrasted with the black circle that extends from its bill to the lower throat, and with the dark markings on its flanks. Its bright red legs and bill add a note of color to its plumage.

The chukar partridge, a native of dry, extremely arid uplands, in its Eurasian home, has adapted well to similar terrain on the North American continent. It must be near a source of water during the hot summer months when the young are growing. At other times of the year, it ranges more freely, usually in coveys of up to forty birds.

In states where it has become well established, the chukar partridge is a gamebird. —G.B.S.

Gray Partridge

Other Common Names—Hungarian partridge
Scientific Name—*Perdix perdix*
Family—Phasianidae (quails, pheasant, and peacocks)
Order—Galliformes
Size—Length, 12 to 13 inches
Range—Europe. Introduced successfully into the Great Plains, Great Basin, and Great Lakes regions

Attempts to establish the European chukar partridge in the United States date to 1893. Only in the Great Basin have these attempts been successful

A gray-brown bird of open, cultivated country, the gray partridge is distinguished by its reddish face and a dark chestnut arc on its light gray underparts. It prefers cool climates, and apparently has little trouble surviving the severe blizzards of its adopted home.

The bulk of the diet of this bird is grain. Insects in summer and buds in winter supplement its basic diet. Males are combative in the spring during pair formation, but coveys of mixed sexes of 30 birds are not uncommon at other times of the year.

Gray partridges were introduced to this continent by sportsmen, and may be hunted in some states.

The name partridge is incorrectly applied to ruffed grouse in some sections of North America. –G.B.S.

PAURAQUE (*See under Whip-poor-will*)

Campo pea

PEA
Campo Pea
Other Common Names—Pride of California
Scientific Name—*Lathyrus splendens*
Family—Leguminosae (pulse family)
Range—San Diego County, California, south to northern Baja California
Habitat—Hillsides, Upper Sonoran Zone
Time of Blooming—April to June

In the mountains of southern San Diego County near Campo is this lovely red sweet pea. It makes a trail of arresting color as it throws its tendrils over shrubs and low trees, the crimson of its blossoms being most unusual. This plant very closely resembles our cultivated sweat pea, having five petals—the upper one called the banner, the two side ones the wings, and the two lower ones with joined edges the keel. On the seashore, above Santa Cruz the beach pea, *Lathyrus littoralis,* grows, creeping, rather hairy, the banner purple, the wings and keel white; on the Humboldt coast the *Lathyrus torreyi,* occurs not a foot tall, the leaves lastingly fragrant, banner pale lilac, wings and keel white; in northern open forests from 4,000 to 6,000 feet elevations, and in the Sierra Nevada *Lathyrus graminifolius* grows, white with flush of pink; from Monteray south over the Tehachapi Mountains to San Diego the species *Lathyrus strictus* grows, in shades of rose with red or purple markings.

PEARL (*See under Bivalve; and under Mollusk*)

PECAN
Other Common Names—Sweet pecan
Scientific Name—*Carya illinoensis*
Family—Juglandaceae (walnut family)
Range—From southwestern Wisconsin and southwestern Indiana south to western Alabama, and west to eastern Iowa, central Kansas, and central Texas, including lower Rio Grande Valley and Mexico. Also widely planted, north to Virginia
Habitat—Bottomlands
Leaves—Compound, 12 to 20 inches long with 9 to 17 fairly narrow, pointed leaflets with toothed edges (much like butternut hickory)
Bark—Gray to gray-brown, moderately rough with age
Flower—Male: consisting of sizable greenish catkins (to five inches) like those of other hickories. Female: inconspicuous
Fruit—In clusters, with fairly thin husks that split into four sections, releasing the smooth, football-shaped nuts. Husks often remain on the twigs

Throughout its natural and cultivated range the pecan is strictly a southern tree. It is a member of the hickory tribe, but one whose rather brittle wood has small rating compared to the value of its well-known and tasty nuts. It is sometimes planted as a shade and yard tree with, of course, the added dividend of its fruit, but the greater number of pecans are seen as groves, orchards, or as plantations of considerable size. The rather spreading, evenly balanced form of such trees is usually recognizable at a distance and many of them grow to

Pecan (above); redbud (below)

considerable size—100 feet or so with trunks a full yard in diameter. A few may attain half again these dimensions. Pecan trees growing in the forest are proportionately taller and narrower and can sometimes be recognized by the bark which is cracked into a network of rather small, rough, raised areas not unlike that of the butternut hickory which also has similar leaves.

The pecan is a fast grower when young and may live to an old age (over 350 years) which makes it a still more desirable plantation species, particularly when grown in rather rich soils with an adequate supply of subsurface water. Several varieties have been developed that produce nuts with special traits such as papershell pecans, but many of the nuts sold are from natural grown trees. —M.H.B.

PECCARY
Collared Peccary
Other Common Names—Javelina, musk hog
Scientific Name—*Tayassu tajacu*
Family—Tayassuidae (peccaries)
Order—Artiodactyla
Size—Body length, 30 to 37 inches; height at shoulder, 20 to 22 inches; weight, 40 to 65 pounds
Range—Southeastern Arizona, southwestern and southeastern corner of New Mexico, and central Texas north to the Red River. South through Mexico (except central portion) to Central and South America

The peccary is the only native North American animal that can be called "wild pig." While it is true that the collared peccary closely resembles the Old World pigs in appearance and the relationship is reasonably close, it belongs in a separate and distinct family of its own.

The peccary is mainly a South and Central American mammal. There are two species, the white-lipped peccary, *Tayassu pecari,* and the collared peccary, *T. tajacu,* but only the latter ranges north to southern Texas, New Mexico, and Arizona. It is piglike in general appearance with a long muzzle, fairly large ears, long coarse pelage, and a short tail. The white-lipped peccary is almost black with a white lip, while the collared peccary is grizzled and has a distinct collar of light-colored hairs across its shoulders. The female has but two young annually; they are reddish in color and quite different from the drab appearance of their parents. The peccary, while primarily herbivorous, feeding mostly on roots and vegetable matter, will devour almost any kind of small animal life found on and in the soil.

The collared peccary resembles the Old World pigs but is classified in a family of its own

Peccaries travel in small bands, usually frequenting valleys and plains where dense thickets of cacti and mesquite afford them shelter and safety. They have a reputation for being dangerous if molested, but under normal circumstances are shy and anxious to escape from man.

PEEPER (*See under Tree Frog*)

PELECYPOD (*See Bivalve*)

PELICAN

Pelicans are large birds that inhabit the temperate and tropical regions of both hemispheres. They are birds of great size, some having wingspans of almost 10 feet. All of the pelicans have large, pouched bills with which they catch fish by scooping them from the water or by diving. The flexible pouch is attached along the entire length of the bill and when not filled with water and fishes is retracted. The pouches may be as long as 15 inches and up to 6 inches in depth and often exceed a capacity of 12 quarts.

Two of the eight species of pelicans inhabit the United States. The white pelican, *Pelecanus erythrorhyncos,* with its nine foot wingspread inhabits inland waters where it breeds in colonies of thousands. The brown pelican, *P. occidentalis,* is associated with the sea, and its breeding colonies are situated on rocky islands along the West Coast and from the southeastern United States south to South America. It is somewhat smaller than its relative the white pelican; its wingspread of 6½ feet more closely approximates that of an eagle.

–G.A.B.

Brown pelicans

Brown Pelican
Other Common Names—Common pelican
Scientific Name—*Pelecanus occidentalis*
Family—Pelecanidae (pelicans)
Order—Pelecaniformes
Size—Length, 50 inches
Range—Southern British Columbia south along the Pacific Coast to southern Chile. Atlantic Coast from North Carolina and Gulf Coast south to West Indies and the coasts of Central and South America to British Guiana and occasionally extreme northern Brazil

The brown pelican is a salt water bird and does all its fishing in coastal waters. Unlike the white pelican, this bird hunts singly and with an entirely different technique. Pulling its head and neck in close to its body it dives into the sea, sometimes from great heights, with its wings partially folded. The bird often hits the water with such force that it is completely hidden by a spray of seawater. The impact stuns fish as much as six feet below the surface. A series of air sacs in the skin of the pelican's breast probably serve to protect it from the shock of hitting the water.

Brown pelicans are often met by gulls when they come up with a fish. Before the pelican can fly away it must adjust its catch, usually transferring it to its gullet, and eject the seawater it has collected along with its prey. The gull

White pelicans are birds of inland waters

hovers over the pelican and sometimes even sits on its large bill. When the pelican opens its mouth to expel the seawater, the gull reaches in and snatches the fish, leaving the helpless pelican to try again.

On some islands along the coast of the southern United States the brown pelican sometimes nests in mangrove trees where it builds a bulky nest of sticks. In other places the nest is a less complex affair of a simple hollow scratched out on low sandbars and lined with a few feathers, twigs, and coarse grasses. Often the eggs laid on the ground are washed away by floods. The pelicans do not attempt to save their eggs when this happens, but they sometimes lay two or three coarse, white eggs again.

Adult brown pelicans have white heads with a slightly yellow tinge on the crown. Their necks are a chestnut color, grading to brown on the body. Their bills are mottled gray with spots of red, and their pouches are black. In the winter months most of the neck is white.
—G.A.B.

White Pelican
Other Common Names—American white pelican
Scientific Name—*Pelecanus erythrorhynchos*
Family—Pelecanidae (pelicans)
Order—Pelecaniformes
Size—Length, 60 inches
Range—Breeds from southern Canada, eastern Oregon, northeastern, central and southeastern California to central-western Nevada, southern Montana, northern

Utah, and Wyoming, east-central North Dakota, and northwestern and central South Dakota

White pelicans are birds of inland waters. In former times they were much more common in the eastern United States, but today only an occasional bird is sighted, and the nesting colonies are found no farther east than North Dakota. They nest in great numbers in the interior valleys of the northwestern states and northern California, and on islands in the Great Salt Lake, and other, smaller lakes in Utah and Nevada. It is an interesting fact that these salt lakes are devoid of fishes, and the pelicans must transport food for themselves and their hungry young from distances of 30 to 100 miles.

Breeding colonies are also established at Yellowstone Lake in northwestern Wyoming and at Lake Bowdoin and Big Lake in Stillwater County, Montana, and at Chase Lake in North Dakota and some small lakes in South Dakota. There is also a colony at Laguna de la Madre in southeastern Texas.

White pelicans hunt in groups, flying close together to spread large shadows on the water. The frightened fish are driven into shallow water where the pelicans suddenly swoop down in perfect unison to make the kill. Moving their bills back and forth under water, the pouch is used as a dip net to collect the fishes. When they have caught their prey they usually transfer the fishes to their gullets, eject the water and retract the pouch before flying away.

To feed its young, the large clumsy-looking white pelican regurgitates a soupy mixture of partly digested fishes into its pouch and the young bird nearly disappears into the cavernous mouth of its parent as it eats. The young, a week or two before they are fully fledged, wander about in large groups and rush greedily at the adult birds when they return with the food. Only the parents' own young are fed, however.

The nest of white pelicans is built on

White pelicans

Great numbers of white pelicans nest at Great Salt Lake, Utah

the ground by scraping up a mound of sandy soil about six inches high. A crude platform of sticks and grasses is placed upon this and two or three crusty, white eggs are laid. The eggs are incubated for a period up to six weeks in duration and the young birds spend another five weeks in or near the nest. Both parents incubate the eggs.

One peculiar characteristic of the white pelican is the development of a horny excrescence on the upper bill during the breeding season. It begins to grow on both sexes after the pairs form in the spring and by the time the young hatch may be three inches high and nearly as wide. Before the nesting season is over the "horn" is shed and thousands of these litter the breeding colonies. The purpose of this structure, if any, is not known.

Adult white pelicans have white plumage with black wing coverts. Their heads, lesser wing coverts, and breasts are tinged with straw yellow. Their bills and feet are yellow with a reddish tint and their pouches grade from yellow and orange to red at the base. The bare skin around their eyes is orange. —G.A.B.

Recommended Reading

Birds of America—T. Gilbert Pearson, editor. Garden City Books, Garden City, New York.
Living Birds of the World—E. Thomas Gilliard. Doubleday & Company, Inc., Garden City, New York.

How the Pelican Got Its Name

At least 25 centuries ago, outdoorsmen knew that some birds peck holes in wood. So from *pelekys,* the Greek term for *ax,* any feathered woodcutter was called a *pelekon.* This was the significance of the name as employed by the greatest of early scientists, Aristotle.

Partly as a result of his influence, references to the pelekon crept into varied types of literature. Some authors used the name without having a clear idea as to the bird it indicated. Such was the case with St. Jerome, whose monumental translation of the Bible was standard for many centuries. It included a reference that, when later rendered into English, became "pelican of the wilderness."

English readers had no notion of what that bird might be like. Some time later after A.D. 1400, they became acquainted with a big-billed fellow that has a pouch for storing fish. Perhaps this odd specimen was a pelican! Once christened in such informal fashion, the name stuck—in spite of the fact that no pelican has a beak designed to serve as an ax.

—W.B.G.

White pelican, showing the horny excrescence on its upper bill, from Audubon's Elephant Folio

PENICILLIN

A drug of nearly miraculous effectiveness against a number of bacterial infections, penicillin is obtained from a primitive plant of the fungi group that is one of the blue-green molds that attack nearly any damp surface of organic matter.

In 1928 it was observed that bacteria did not survive near colonies of *Penicillium,* but it was not until 1941 that extracts from the liquid in which the mold had been grown were used on human beings. The substance proved to be lethal to staphylococcus, streptococcus, pneumococcus, and the bacteria that causes gas gangrene, to name a few.

The drug itself is prepared in modern laboratories under rigorously controlled procedures from *Penicillium notatum.* It is one of the most effective antibiotics yet developed. (*See also under Fungus*) —G.B.S.

PENTSTEMON

Heart-leaved Pentstemon

Other Common Names—Climbing pentstemon, honeysuckle pentstemon

Scientific Name—*Pentstemon cordifolius*

Family—Scrophulariaceae (figwort family)

Range—Coastal mountains of southern California from San Luis Obispo County to Mexican border

Habitat—Chaparral slopes, Upper Sonoran Zone

Time of Blooming—May to June

The flower of the heart-leaved pentstemon is a long scarlet tube with an upper lip showing two lobes and a lower one showing three. Five stamens rise from the throat, two curving upward on each side and closely laid against the upper lip, the fifth stamen being sterile and often heavily bearded. The name is from the Greek *pente,* five, and *stemon,* stamen. The five stamens always curve up flat against the upper petals. The leaves are heart-shaped. This pentstemon is like a woody vine, and climbs over fences and small shrubs.

Heart-leaved pentstemon

There are half a hundred pentstemons, some of them being shrubs. In early summer in dry hills and valleys the rather strange color combination of a red-purple tube, topped by lips of definite blue, mark the species, *Pentstemon spectabilis,* often attaining a height of five feet; on mesas and flats the evergreen shrub *Pentstemon antirrhinoides* occurs, with its long, graceful branches covered with wide-mouthed yellow flowers; in late summer on the roads to northern lakes above Mono are companies of bewitching beauty, the flowers frequently two inches long—pink, lavender, purple.

PEONY
Western Peony
Other Common Names—None
Scientific Name—*Paeonia brownii*
Family—Ranunculaceae (crowfoot family)
Range—Eastern slopes of Cascade Mountains and Blue Mountains, southeastern Washington south through the Cascades and the Sierra Nevadas to the mountains of southern California east to Utah
Habitat—Rocky ridges, Hudsonian and Canadian zones—Hudsonian Zone near the confines of perpetual snow on the subalpine range of Mount Hood
Time of Blooming—June to July

Western peony

Soon after the cold winter rains are over the western peony pushes up its leaves. They are broad and have scarlet tips. As they grow they separate into many sections. Then the flowers come. They are easy to see from the roadside, for the petals are dark wine color. They are thick and like leather. In the center there are many yellow stamens and several little round green balls which are seedpods. As the seedpods ripen they become heavy, often causing the flower to rest on the ground. The root is very thick. The plant grows on bushy hillslopes.

PEOPLE AND INSECTS (*See under Insect: Insect Control; and under Insect: Insect Values*)

PEPPERIDGE (*See under Tupelo*)

PERCH
Yellow Perch
Other Common Names—Ringed perch; common perch; ring-tail perch; lake perch
Scientific Name—*Perca flavescens*
Family—Percidae (perches)
Order—Perciformes
Size—Length, 15 inches
Range—Fresh waters of ponds and streams throughout southern Canada and south to Kansas, Missouri, Illinois, Ohio, and Pennsylvania. Also in streams of Atlantic coastal drainage from Nova Scotia to South Carolina. Artificially introduced elsewhere

The yellow perch's mouth has many small teeth. The fish has two well separated dorsal fins. The front one usually has 12 or 13 spiny rays. The rear one has soft rays. The anal fin has six to eight rays and is preceded by two spines.

The fish's back is brassy green to rich yellow. Its sides are lighter. Six to nine black or dark olive bands cross the back and sides perpendicularly. The belly is white to yellow.

The yellow perch eats small fishes, insects, young crayfishes, scuds, and

Yellow perch

snails. It is a favorite game fish and makes very fine eating (*See also under Fish: Common Freshwater Fishes of North America*).

The white perch, *Roccus americanus*, another fine game fish, is actually a bass (*See under Bass*). Other fishes with the common name *perch* include the pirate perch, *Aphredoderus sayanus*, and the trout-perch, *Percopsis omiscomaycus*.
—M.R.

PERCH: *White Perch* (*See under Bass*)

PEREGRINE (*See under Falcon*)

PERSIMMON

Two persimmons are native to North America. The common persimmon, *Diospyros virginiana*, that ranges from New Jersey to Nebraska south, is an attractive tree often 40 feet tall, with glossy, simple, alternate leaves. The sap is white and sticky, and the flattened globular fruits are astringent until ripened by frost. Male and female flowers occur on different trees.

The black persimmon, a smaller species, grows in Texas and in Mexico. Persimmons sold in the market are of another species, the Japanese persimmon.

These trees are members of the family Ebenaceae, a tropical group whose most famous member is the ebony tree of southern Asia.
—G.B.S.

The common persimmon and its distribution

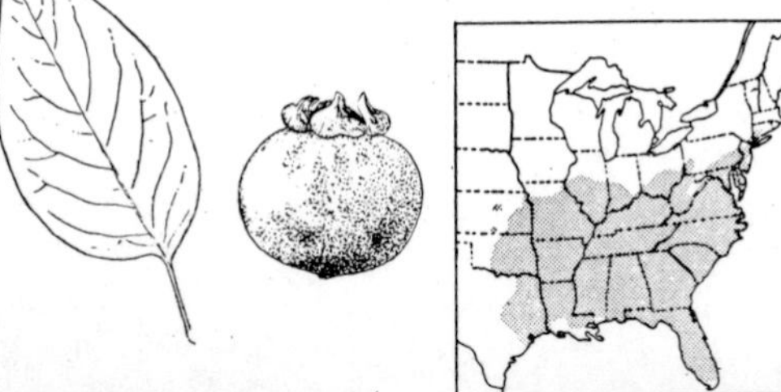

PESTICIDE

A pesticide is any agent, usually a chemical, used to kill pests. Since insects are the most common organisms considered pests, the insecticides are the commonest pesticides. In addition, however, the term pesticide includes fungicides (to kill fungi, molds, rusts), herbicides (to kill plants), and rodenticides (to kill rodents).

Because many of the synthetic chemicals used as pesticides are broad-spectrum poisons, they have been called biocides—killers of life. Their use imposes a serious responsibility. In general, pesticides should be used only in minimum quantities necessary to do the job. The pesticide should also be short-lived. Any poison or application that is less selective threatens to poison the landscape and impoverish the environment, since there are infinitely more beneficial organisms than there are pests (*See Insecticide*).
—R.C.C.

PET ANIMALS: *Wild Pets* (*See under Kangaroo Rat; also Mammal: Care of Mammal Pets*)

PETREL

Of the 23 species of storm petrels in the world, only 5 species and 2 subspecies are common in the waters off the coasts of North America. They are Leach's and Wilson's petrels on the Atlantic, and the fork-tailed, black, and ashy petrels on the Pacific Coast. Beal's and Socorro petrels are subspecies of Leach's petrel that differ from the other Pacific Coast species.

All of these birds strongly resemble Leach's petrel in size, silhouette, and habits. Wilson's petrel has a square tail and a swallowlike flight; Leach's has a forked tail and a bouncy motion in flight.

The fork-tailed petrel is pearly gray, and is the only petrel so colored. Beal's petrel is the only petrel of the Pacific Coast with a black body and a white rump. The other three are all black. The largest is the black petrel, nine inches in length with long wings and a ternlike flight. The Socorro petrel is second in size, just under eight inches, with shorter wings and a more direct flight; it sometimes has a bit of white on the rump. The ashy petrel is 7½ inches long, with short wings and a fluttering flight. Most individuals have some white under the wings. The legs of the ashy petrel are very short. —G.B.S.

Leach's Petrel
Other Common Names—White-rumped petrel, Leach's fork-tailed petrel
Scientific Name—*Oceanodroma leucorhoa*
Family—Hydrobatidae (storm petrels)
Order—Procellariiformes
Size—Length, 8 inches
Range—Northern Japan and Aleutian Islands south along Pacific Coast to Baja California west to Gallapagos and Hawaiian Islands. Atlantic Ocean from

Leach's petrel does not follow ships and is usually seen at a distance

Labrador, Iceland, and the Faeroes south to Massachusetts and Ireland and to the equator and occasionally the Gold Coast and South Africa

Life Story of Leach's Petrel

There is still much to be learned about the Leach's petrel, but the accumulated observer records reveal a fascinating life history. About the size of a catbird, the petrel is a small but true bird of the ocean. The vast salt deep is its principal haunt, for there it spends most of its life. From the ocean it takes its food and drink. It comes to land only to nest and rear its young. Men of science have indicated its oceanic attachment by giving it the generic name *Oceonodroma—ocean running.*

To sailors of the British Isles and their descendants on the Atlantic Coast of North America, the bird is known as Mother Carey's chicken or kerry chicken. If sailors use the name petrel at all, it is then dramatically qualified as *stormy petrel,* although this seaman's term is used generally and not specifically to identify the species known to science as storm petrel.

The Leach's petrel is equally at home in the Atlantic and Pacific. In the Atlantic Ocean it wanders northward to Iceland and southward to the equator; in the Pacific, north to the Bering Sea and south to the Galapagos and Hawaiian Islands. Its breeding areas are scattered around the globe. In the eastern Atlantic, it nests on a few islands off Iceland and the northwest coast of Scotland; also in the Mediterranean Sea. In the western Atlantic, it nests on islands from Greenland to Maine and Massachusetts. In the Pacific, it nests in the Kurile, Aleutian, and Alaskan Islands.

These breeding areas are determined, perhaps, by the location of the oceanic pastures that the birds frequent. Two British ornithologists, John A. Ainslie and Robert Atkinson, who have made a study of this petrel in the North Atlantic, found that nesting colonies occur only in the region of the greatest density of plankton—those minute and free floating organisms that form the great pastures of the sea (*See under Plankton*).

Not everything is known about the food habits of the Leach's petrel, but it is known that it feeds mostly on a variety of these plankton forms, minute crustaceans including copepods, tiny fishes, small squids, and globules of oil

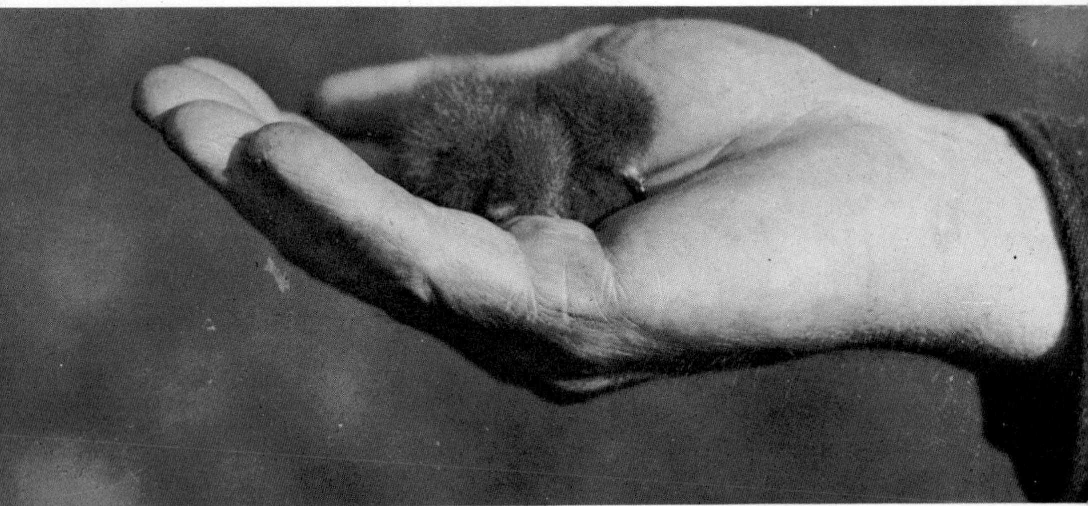

The incubation period of the single Leach's petrel chick is between 35 and 42 days. It does not leave its nesting burrow for another 50 days

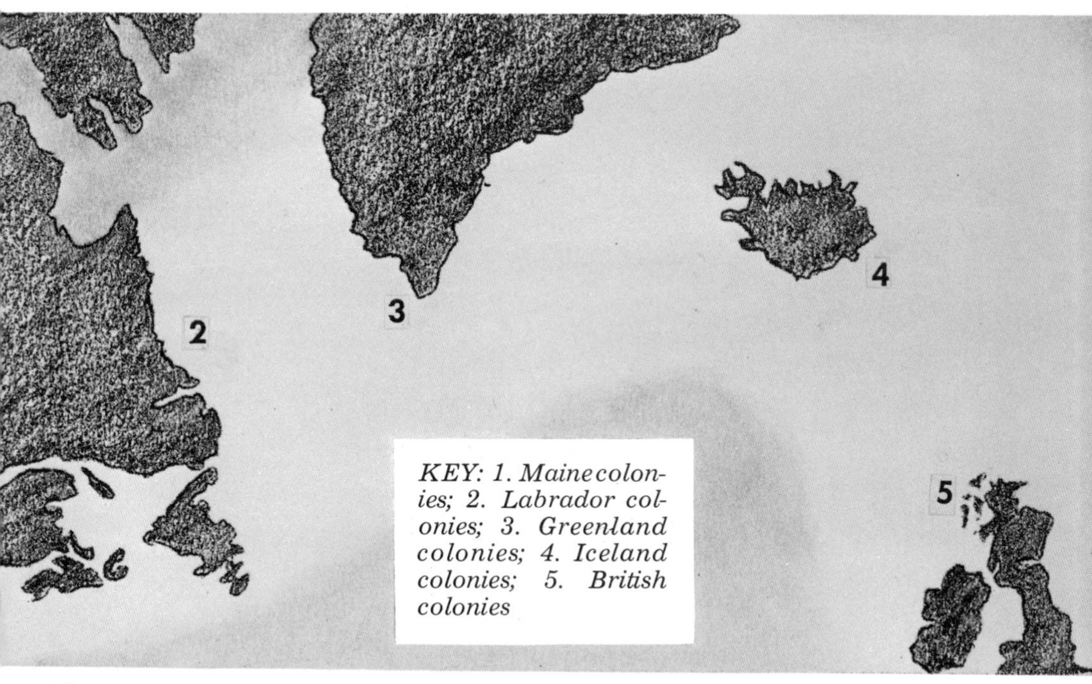

The distribution of the Leach's petrel's breeding colonies lies within the area of greatest plankton density, indicated here by a light band

and greasy waste matter from fishes, seals, and whales. Through the process of digestion this food becomes an oily, orange-colored liquid. Often when the birds are disturbed by enemies or handled by man they eject this acrid, musky smelling fluid from the mouth in a sudden squirt. It is thought that this habit of vomiting is a protective device, as the liquid can cause temporary blindness in an enemy.

While the ocean provides food in plenty and a way of life for the petrel, it fails the bird in one crucial aspect. It cannot provide a nesting site. The petrel must have a place in which to dig a burrow and rear its only young one, and for this purpose it must return to land. The petrel's link with the land is also a link with man, for it is during the nesting season that this amazing bird can best be observed. On the outer islands of Maine, the petrels return to breed in mid-May, when the deep-set frosts have melted.

When the bird turns to its task of building a nest, it digs with feet and bill to make a burrow of from two to four feet in length that terminates in a somewhat larger cavity, the nest chamber. Apparently, little of the loose earth is removed from the burrow but is packed down by the little flat webbed feet. The entrance tunnels are from two to four inches wide and are never straight, but turn right and left, sometimes quite sharply. When the snug chamber is ready, the female petrel lays a single white egg.

The survival of a species that lays only one egg a year is a remarkable thing, yet this is characteristic of all the petrels, from the tiny storm petrels of the waters of Great Britain to the giant albatrosses of the Pacific. Whether or not a second egg is produced if the first is taken or destroyed is still a mystery. Be this as it may it is certain that only one chick is ever found in a burrow, and so the maximum reproduction rate of this species is one bird per pair per year. Naturally, this optimum rate is never achieved, for sometimes eggs are infertile and sometimes chicks die in the burrows—victims of starvation and lack of brooding. The survival powers of the petrel must be extraordinary to permit it to maintain successful population numbers at all.

The egg is about the size of a robin's. Usually, the larger the bird, the longer the incubation period: the robin averages 14 days; the herring gull, 28; the bald eagle, 35. But although the Leach's petrel is smaller than a robin, its incubation covers the astonishingly long period of 35 to 42 days and perhaps longer. No one has yet definitely established the exact length of time, but it is known to be from five to six weeks.

Both parents share the task—one remaining in the nest while the other is gathering food at sea.

As a result of this long development within the egg, a most curious chick emerges. Covered with gray down, it looks like a ball of fluff—like something that came out of a vacuum cleaner. From this spherical shape protrudes a sharp black tube-nosed bill, giving the impression of an afterthought, for the creature is so round and so covered with long filaments that it appears to have no head.

Growth and development of the chick is astonishingly slow. While the robin is fully fledged and leaves the nest within 14 days of being hatched, the young petrel remains in its dark burrow for at least 50 days. On the Maine Coast islands, petrel chicks are regularly found in the burrows not only throughout September and October, but in some cases as late as December. William A.O. Gross, in his studies at Kent's Island, Bay of Fundy, concluded that the full growth of a petrel, including the incubation period, takes about 120 days.

This slow development may be attributed to irregular and interrupted provision of food by the adults. Students of the petrel have found that after the chicks are several weeks old, they are quite frequently left alone for two or three days at a time. The experimenters discovered this by the ingenious device of placing twigs, matchstick size, across the entrances to the burrows.

That the young live in darkness for such a long period is a remarkable fact. Yet darkness is an essential circumstance in petrel life. In darkness the adults first return to their breeding haunts; in darkness the burrow is excavated; in darkness the chick is born and reared and, when it emerges for the first time into the upper and outer world, it flies off to the ocean in the darkness of the night. The young bird first sees the light of day not on land, but at sea.

In October, while there are still chicks in the burrows, the petrels begin to take leave of the Maine coast. In November the colonies thin out rapidly, but chicks have been found as late as December. Until records of nest occupancy later than December are found, it can be presumed that departure for the wintering "grounds" has been completed by the last of the year. Back to the sea, then, for kerry chickens. "Out there" and "down there," as the seamen say—as far down as the equator—the birds wander away their winter, entirely divorced from the land.

Except for storms at sea, little is known of the dangers of petrel life during their miles and months of wandering over the vast waters of the globe. Yet it is nature's inexorable law that there is always "the eater and the eaten." Large fishes may take the birds at sea; other animals that may endanger them is another mystery. Perhaps a scarcity of predators at sea explains their survival.

On the nesting grounds, the petrels become the victims of gulls and other large birds. In Maine, on the Canadian Maritime Provinces, and on the British Isles, the great black-backed gull is the principal predator of Leach's petrel. Although the petrels seek the cover of darkness, a bright moon exposes them to sight, and petrel remains are invariably found in the vicinity of the burrows on the morning after a night of attack by gulls. In an experiment at the Bowdoin Biological Station on Kent's Island, a captive great black-backed gull consumed five adult petrels in 20 minutes.

Through thousands and thousands of years petrel populations have been in balance with the natural dangers involved in their existence. However, the remote islands that they use as breeding grounds are free of the one threat they cannot cope with—land mammals. They know only the mammals of the sea—the seals, the porpoises, and the great whales. On their ancestral breeding grounds there were probably no land mammals of any kind — no weasels, skunks, foxes, minks—to which, as burrow-nesting species, they would have been hopelessly vulnerable.

Long ago, when the northeast coast was still a wilderness, there were many mammal-free islands and many petrel colonies. But when men came to these islands as fishermen and lighthouse keepers, dogs, cats, and sometimes rats and other land mammals came with them. Man alone however, would not have constituted an upsetting factor to the petrels' special ecological equilibrium. This is evident on Little Green Island where the lone lobster fisherman fits undisturbingly into the ecological scene. All around his little one-room house, and even under its very floor, his kerry chickens have their burrows. Off and on, sheep have grazed on Little Green, but they did not disturb the petrels.

Yet on Big Green Island, only several miles away, a fisherman brought, of all mammals, foxes to be raised for commercial purposes. Within a year, the entire petrel colony was extirpated by the foxes. And once a species is driven from its ancestral breeding grounds, it may be many years before it returns, if ever.

Although driven from many of its former breeding grounds, the Leach's petrel is not yet among those birds on the "threatened" list. According to authentic reports, most by Alfred Gross, of Bowdoin College, Maine, it seems that the petrel is just about holding its own. This bird deserves further study. Except for Gross and his son, William A.O. Gross, few ornithologists in America have devoted any major time to research on the Leach's petrel. It may not be long before its last remaining island fastnesses will be assailed by man. Now, before the bird becomes threatened, is the time to establish the protection it needs. —C.B.

How The Petrel Got Its Name

English seamen of the 16th Century took great interest in a bird they saw in the north Atlantic. Sooty black with white markings, the little sea fowl usually flew very low over the water, feeding on small surface-swimming creatures.

Sailors were not interested in the bird's diet, however. They were fascinated by the way it would glide along with wings motionless, seeming to pat the top of the water with its feet. It didn't take a vivid imagination to think of the little creature as walking upon the water.

William Dampier took note of the bird in his book, *A New Voyage Around the World* (1703). Its habits, he said made pious explorers think of the man who walked on the water of a lake. So the name of St. Peter was bestowed upon the water-walking bird. Slightly altered, it became the familiar petrel. —W.B.S.

PETRIFIED FOREST NATIONAL MONUMENT

Location—Eastern Arizona
Size—145 square miles
Mammals—Pronghorns, bobcats, coyo-

A fossilized tree stump at Petrified Forest National Monument, Arizona

tes, foxes, prairie dogs, skunks, pack rats, ground squirrels, cottontails, and jackrabbits

Birdlife—Hawks, owls, roadrunners, quails, many songbirds

Plants—Junipers, greasewood, skunk bushes, sages, cacti, yuccas, mariposa lilies, evening primroses, larkspurs

Over 180 million years ago, in the Triassic Period, forests of cycads and primitive conifers grew along streams and rivers near an inland sea. Some were undercut by the current and carried downstream to rest on sandbars. The sand covered them before they rotted, and their tissues were fossilized—replaced by silica and other elements in the form of agate, jasper, onyx, and opal. In many of them the replacement was so perfect that the individual cells can still be distinguished.

The monument includes a portion of the Painted Desert, where sandstones in hues of red, yellow, brown, and mauve are spectacular in their beauty.

Accommodations—At Holbrook, Arizona, 20 miles away

Headquarters—In the monument; address at Holbrook, Arizona

PEWEE (*See under Wood Pewee*)

PHAINOPEPLA

Other Common Names—Silky flycatcher, shining crested flycatcher

Scientific Name—*Phainopepla nitens*

Family—Ptilogonatidae (silky flycatchers)

Order—Passeriformes

Size—Length, 7¾ inches

Range—Breeds chiefly in arid lowlands

of Arizona, California, southern Nevada, southwestern New Mexico, western Texas, and southern Utah. Breeding birds of California west of the deserts do not arrive until those of the deserts are finishing nesting. Winters in southern Arizona, southern California, and western Texas

Black, slim and shiny, the phainopepla (pronounced fay-een-o-pep-la or fain-o-pepla) is as unique as its strange-sounding name. A glutton for berries, it often makes its headquarters where pepper trees have been planted, or in a mesquite or palo verde thicket where the desert mistletoe grows. After a meal of mistletoe berries, it may wipe its sticky beak on a branch nearby leaving some of the tiny seeds to germinate and produce a new clump of mistletoe. When a phainopepla flies, it flashes great white wing patches as conspicuous as those of a magpie.

The song of the phainopepla is a weak, wheezy, casual warble. Common call notes are a liquid *klip*, and, when alarmed, a harsh *kerrr*.

Phainopepla

PHALAROPE

Shorebirds of the sandpiper and plover order, Charadriiformes, phalaropes have a number of distinctive traits. The toes are lobed, and the birds spend much of their lives, especially in the winter, on the water instead of along the shore. The plumage is exceptionally dense and filled with air, allowing the birds to ride high out of the water. Necks are long in this family, and the head is carried high.

The female is the larger and more colorful of the pair. She performs the courting acts, and leaves it to the male to build the nest and incubate the eggs and care for the young.

There are three north American species of phalaropes. The red phalarope, in its summer home in the Arctic, is reddish below, with a white face; in the winter, floating in rafts far at sea, it is blue-gray above and white below. The bill is yellow and short.

The northern phalarope also breeds in the Arctic. Females are dark gray above, with rufous margins to the white throat front; males are similar, but lighter. Both have a dark bill. In winter both are gray and white, with dark striping on the back.

Wilson's phalarope—gray, rufous, and black, with a pale crown—breeds on the North American prairies and winters in South America. —G.B.S.

Red Phalarope
Other Common Names—Whale bird, gray phalarope
Scientific Name—*Phalaropus fulicarius*
Family—Phalaropodidae (phalaropes)
Order—Charadriiformes
Size—Length, 8½ inches
Range—Arctic Ocean south to Yukon delta, Southampton Island, and Iceland

Phalaropes are masters of the three elements—the air, the earth, and the water. They are swift and graceful on the wing, nimble swimmers when afloat, and as fleet as the liveliest of sandpipers

while ashore. Their interest in the ocean is perennial, but their liking for land lasts only through the season when they are hatching and rearing their young.

The red phalarope, *Phaloropus fulicarius,* is rarely seen inland in the United States. It migrates, usually well offshore, along the Atlantic and Pacific coasts of North America, and winters in the oceans off the coasts of South America. It is casual in migration (inland) in southern California, Colorado, Kansas, Alabama, Vermont, New York, Pennsylvania, Illinois, Ohio, Maryland, and in Ontario, Canada.

The red phalarope is a boreal species seldom found south of the delta of the Yukon or Southampton Island in summer. It is abundant in Greenland, Iceland, and along the frozen shores of Eurasia as far as utmost Siberia. Breeding far up on the top of the world amid icy solitudes from Alaska to Kamchatka, this beautiful species is inaccessible to most people during its nesting season. It is, however, extremely abundant off the Atlantic and Pacific coasts of the United States while it is migrating north in May, usually a hundred miles or more out from shore. Unless driven in by storms the species keeps to deep water.

After mating, the males build the nest, usually a grass-lined depression fairly well concealed in the tundra. There the females lay their eggs, usually four, which are ovate, buffy, and boldly marked with russet and brown, most thickly on the larger ends. Occasional sets of six eggs found in a nest are thought to have been laid by two females.

After the female red phalarope has laid her eggs, her cares are over for the season. She leaves the male to hatch the eggs and goes about with other females that have also laid their eggs. They seldom revisit their nests unless called by sudden danger. The meek little males brood the eggs and care for the chicks after they pip their shells. But they do not have to feed them. In a few hours after hatching, the young can find their own provender. They learn to paddle and plunge on secluded inland pools, where

they often spin like whirligig beetles, kicking up the mud to rout the larvae of insects which they eat. They can also tip up like puddle ducks, and dabble deftly below the surface of the water for their food.

Their summer diet includes midges and other insects which the chicks snatch greedily. They also eat bloodworms, jellyfishes, leaches, and minnows. After leaving the land their diet becomes strictly marine. On masses of gulfweed they find plenty of mollusks, minute crabs, and larvae (*See Plankton*).

They are adept in caring for themselves by the time the various families are ready to start their 3,500-mile southern trek.

Although only 7½ to 9 inches in length, the red phalarope is admirably equipped for a marine life. Its feet are only slightly palmated but strongly lobed, so that it can swim or dive like a sea duck. Its breast and underparts are densely feathered, covering a layer of body down, so that it can withstand cold water as well as any wildfowl.

Nobody has yet traced the wanderings of the red phalarope. Late in the summer single birds or small fleets of them appear off Cape Anne, Cape Cod, Monomoy, and Montauk, off the coasts of Massachusetts and Long Island, New York, but not in the gaudy plumage of spring. It is the same way with the larger flocks passing down the coasts of Washington, Oregon, and California. Already both sexes show prevailingly white or gray, with mere touches of color.

After leaving its northern nesting grounds it becomes truly cosmopolitan and is seen on all the northern oceans, and in the Mediterranean, off the Azores, in the Indian Ocean, China Sea, and along the coasts of Africa. It has been recorded as far south as Patagonia, and is casual in California, Colorado, Kansas, Alabama, New York, Pennsylvania, and Maryland. Unless driven in by unusual storms, however, it does not enter the bays and estuaries of New England and the Middle Atlantic States. Always and everywhere, after the breeding season the red phalarope is a coastwise migrant, keeping well offshore.

This does not mean that the species is shy and retiring. It is always tame and allows one to row up behind it in a dory and watch its movements. If it flutters away from the boat it promptly alights and goes on feeding as usual. It bobs about like a tinted cork, riding high, and more like a miniature gull than a beach waif.

To American whalers the red phalarope was always a good omen. Flocks of phalaropes often followed right and bowhead whales, which they seemed to sight underwater long before the masthead man bellowed "Thar she bloows!" (*See under Whales, Dolphins, and Porpoises*)

Arriving on the spot when the whale came to the surface, the phalaropes commenced feeding on the animalcules always to be found swimming near. Whales and shorebirds share their feasts, since the largest of all animals subsist on the smallest of living organisms. And so red phalaropes were well named whalebirds or bowhead birds. —H.M.H.

PHEASANT

Ring-necked Pheasant

Other Common Names—Common pheasant

Scientific Name—*Phasianus colchicus*

Family—Phasianidae (quails, pheasants, and peacocks)

Order—Galliformes

Size—Male: length, 35 inches; female somewhat smaller

Range—Introduced from Asia. South and south central Canada south to Washington, Oregon, Idaho, Montana, eastern Wyoming, Colorado, New Mexico, the panhandle of Texas and Oklahoma, lowlands of California, Utah (excluding mountains and deserts), Nevada, south-

In the 1880's the ring-necked pheasant was successfully introduced into Oregon and has become established in open agricultural country throughout North America

western Arizona, and Baja California. Also from Minnesota, Wisconsin, Michigan, New York, and south central Maine south to Vermont, New Hampshire, Ohio, Pennsylvania, New Jersey, northern Maryland, southern Illinois, Indiana, Kansas, and Missouri

The range of this adaptable bird, a native of Asia, extends from the eastern shores of the Black Sea (Asia Minor) to Japan. It was successfully introduced into North America in the 1880's. The pheasant is presumably now well established in almost every part of the North American continent, where suitable climatic conditions and habitats exist.

The pheasant is primarily a bird of open agricultural country. During the summer it nests in the dense cover of hay, alfalfa, and clover fields. It is a prolific bird, laying about a dozen eggs. Early mowing of fields often results in great losses of breeding females and young.

The summer food includes a wide variety of items—wild fruits, berries, insects, and even mice. Occasionally the pheasant damages such vegetable crops as tomatoes, peas, beans, and corn. During severe winters, pheasants in most areas turn to waste grain and old corn shocks.

The cock pheasant has a loud crow like that of a young bantam rooster, accompanied by an audible flapping of the wings. When alarmed the bird utters a loud series of hoarse croaks as it flies off.

PHLOX

Prickly Phlox

Other Common Names—Gilia

Scientific Name—*Leptodactylon californicum*

Family—Polemoniaceae (polemonium family)

Range—South coast ranges in California from San Luis Obispo County to the Santa Monica Mountains

Habitat—Coastal mesas and canyons and in the chaparral. Upper Sonoran Zone

Prickly phlox

Time of Blooming—March to June

This erect little shrub, from one to three feet high, is very common on hillsides and in washes, and is an early spring bloomer. The stems are reddish-brown. The dark green leaves are short, stiff and in small bunches on the stem, standing out like the bristles of a brush. The flowers are pink, lavender, or rose.

In the higher mountains in midsummer at an altitude of from 9,000 to 12,000 feet the granite gilia, *Leptodactylon pungens,* forms mats of silver gray over granite rocks, the flowers of white or light yellow rising on stems only a few inches above the flat leaf masses. Another member of this family is our highest altitude bloomer, the lovely blue alpine, phlox, *Polemonium confertum,* which holds court at an elevation of 13,000 feet. It is so extremely fragrant that its presence is known long before one comes in sight of it.

The phlox of our gardens is a relative of these flowers.

PHOEBE

Eastern Phoebe
Other Common Names – Pewee, dusty flycatcher
Scientific Name – *Sayornis phoebe*
Family – Tyrannidae (tyrant flycatchers)
Order – Passeriformes
Size – Length, 6½ to 7 inches
Range – Breeds from central Mackenzie, central Manitoba, central Ontario, southern Quebec, and Nova Scotia south to the mountains of Georgia, northern Mississippi, southeastern Colorado, central Texas, and eastern New Mexico. Winters in the southern United States and northern Mexico, but an occasional bird will spend the winter as far north as southern Pennsylvania and New York

The eastern phoebe is a flycatcher that comes north in the spring before insects are abundant. It pushes northward during the wet days of early March. Its early arrival often is disastrous. A late winter snowstorm has been fatal to many an early phoebe that would have done better to arrive a week or two later, at the same time as its mate.

Year after year a pair of eastern phoebes will return to the same spot. Old barns, sheds, abandoned cabins, and culverts that span little streams are favorite home sites. In fact, phoebes are so invariably associated with small bridges that in some sections they have been called *bridge birds*. There they can be found sitting upright on a twig over the water, twitching their tails and calling *phoebe-phoebe*. They are gray-brown birds with white underparts.

The eastern phoebe's upright posture is strictly a flycatcher position. Perching with drooping tail it sits quietly until a small insect buzzes by. With a quick swoop, and a click of the bill, it snaps up the insect in midair, and immediately returns to its post. If a struggling fly is borne downstream beneath the bridge, it darts down and snatches it up from the rippling torrent without wetting a feather. Nine-tenths of the phoebe's food is made up of insects, mostly flying ones, but some caterpillars are also eaten. The other one-tenth of the phoebe's diet is wild berries and seeds, which it can always obtain when insects are scarce.

In the days before there were barns and before bridges were built across streams, the phoebe lived in ravines where rocky walls had been carved out by the water. There it built its nest, tucking it beneath some exposed root or fastening it to a narrow ledge, safe from rain or dripping water. Many phoebes still live in such places, but today most of their nests are built under bridges. Phoebes not only come back to the same spot year after year, but will build their nests on the same ledge or rafter, often using the remains of the previous year's nest for a foundation.

Its nest is well constructed. It is bulky, but it is firm. It is made largely of mud and moss. There, on the soft lining of grass and feathers, three to six pure white eggs are laid. For a small bird—eastern phoebes are between 6½ to 7 inches long—the incubation period is rather long, about 16 days. Like other flycatchers, the young birds stay in the nest longer than the young of robins or most other small birds. After they leave, they sometimes return to the nest at night to roost. Most other young birds abandon the nest for good once they leave. The young phoebes must leave eventually, however, because their parents usually start a second brood.

In about September the ranks of the eastern phoebes thin out. A few birds are seen in October, but by that time most of them have left for the southern United States and northern Mexico. Rarely one is found in winter as far north as Ohio, Pennsylvania, or southern New York.

Two other species of phoebe inhabit

Eastern phoebe

North America. The black phoebe, *Sayornis nigricans,* is at home in the southwestern United States south to central and southern America, and the Say's phoebe, *S. saya,* ranges from central Alaska and western Canada south to Zacatecas and Durango, Mexico. – A. B., Jr.

PHOTOSYNTHESIS (*See under Tree: A Tree in the Forest*)

PHOTOGRAPHY (*See Nature Photography*)

PICKEREL (*See under Pike*)

PICKERELWEED

Other Common Names – Common pickerelweed
Scientific Name – *Pontederia cordata*
Family – Pontederiaceae (pickerelweed family)
Range – Prince Edward Island to southern Ontario, south to Nova Scotia, New England, Long Island, northern Florida, Missouri, and Oklahoma
Habitat – Muddy shores or shallow water
Time of Blooming – June to November

The home of this plant, with its tall spike of blue flowers, is in shallow, freshwater ponds, lakes, and along margins of streams. The flowers are small but under a hand lens their blue anthers and deep blue petals, with a yellow spot at their base, are very beautiful. They are crowded together on the top of a spike that rises a foot or more above the water. The leaves stand erect. The lower lobes of the leaves are rounded and need not be confused with the arrowhead leaves that have pointed lower lobes. These two plants commonly grow in intermingled colonies.

Pickerel fishes frequent areas where these plants grow and no doubt it is from this fact that the name pickerelweed has been derived. As the pickerelweed attracts insects so the insects in turn may attract some fishes.

The color blue, as in the flower of the pickerelweed, is particularly attractive to bees. Once the insect is on the bloom the yellow spot at the base of each petal serves as a guide to the nectar. There are three types of pickerelweed flowers, each growing on separate plants, with the pistil growing to one of three lengths and the stamens growing to two or three lengths in each – a condition known as *heterostyly*. Pollen is dusted on the insect's body in such a way that it will be transferred only to stigmas at a corresponding height in the next plant the insect visits. Thus the most effective cross-fertilization is accomplished.

Cast shells of mayfly and dragonfly nymphs are often found clinging to the leaves of this plant. These shells were

Pickerelweed

abandoned by their nymphal owners when they left their water home to spend the rest of their days in the air.

The black and wood ducks eat pickerelweed seeds to a small extent. Along the Gulf Coast 5 to 10 percent of the mottled ducks' food has been found to be the seed of this plant. Muskrats also eat its seed.

There are only a few species of pickerelweeds and they all grow in America. In eastern United States *Pontederia cordata* is the common species.

PIGEON (*See under Dove*)

PIGEON HORNTAIL

Other Common Names—Pigeon tremex
Scientific Name—*Tremex columba*
Family—Siricidae (wood wasps, horntails)
Order—Hymenoptera
Size—Length, two inches or less
Range—Throughout most of the United States

Horntails are closely related to the sawflies (*See Sawfly*). Like the sawflies, the horntails can be distinguished from other Hymenoptera by the thick waist, as contrasted with the slender stemlike waist of the bees, ants, and wasps. The horntails are large and dull-colored or brilliantly metallic-colored. They are wasplike insects and the long body is terminated in both sexes by a stout spine. The females, in addition, have a long, slender ovipositor. Both of these characters have given them the common name of horntail.

The female horntails when laying their eggs seek out injured or dead trees and insert the ovipositor under the bark or into the wood. Once the ovipositor is inserted it may not be removed quickly and some of the females are thus easily captured as they struggle to free themselves.

After hatching, the pale, cylindrical, S-shaped larvae make large burrows in the sapwood and heartwood of conifers and deciduous trees that are injured or have recently been killed. After reaching their full growth within the tree, the larvae pupate in parchmentlike cocoons within their burrows in the wood before emerging as adults. Restricted to forests and seldom abundant, the horntails are regarded by many entomologists as rather minor pests of forest trees.

Pigeon horntail

The larvae of the pigeon horntail are often parasitized by the larvae of an ichneumon wasp, or ichneumon "fly," *Megarhyssa macrurus*. The female ichneumon can locate a horntail burrow, which is only about half an inch wide, under several inches of wood, and it is not known precisely how she does it. Her ovipositor is unusually long in relation to her body length and is very delicate, yet she is able to pierce solid wood in order to lay an egg within the burrow of the pigeon horntail. The eggs are not necessarily laid near the larvae of the pigeon horntail, but when the ichneumon eggs hatch, the larvae manage to reach the pigeon horntail larvae and devour them (*See also under Biological Control*).

Although the ichnuemon (*Megarhyssa*) is a formidable looking creature, she neither stings humans nor does harm to the trees in which she lays her eggs.

—J.K.T.

Recommended Reading

Field Book of Insects—Frank E. Lutz. G. P. Putman's Sons, New York.
The Insect Guide—Ralph B. Swain. Doubleday & Company, Inc., New York.

The tailless pika looks like a guinea pig; however it is related to rabbits and hares

PIKA
Other Common Names—Cony, rock rabbit, whistling hare
Scientific Name—*Ochotona princeps*
Family—Ochotonidae (pikas)
Order—Lagomorpha
Size—Body length, 7 to 8½ inches; weight, 4½ to 6 ounces
Range—Mountainous regions of western North America from northern New Mexico and Kern River, California, north to southwestern Alberta and southern British Columbia

Among the jumbled boulders of high mountain rock slides little stacks of green vegetation are sometimes to be seen. One has to search carefully to locate the owner of these "hay" piles. Usually its bleating call, a high-pitched, nasal *eenk*, gives it away—a hunched-up little ball of fur perched inconspicuously on a rock. This is a pika, and the piles of alpine heather, lupine, grasses, sedges, and other vegetation are its autumn harvest. In winter the rockslides will be buried deep under the snow, and as the pika does not hibernate, these "haystacks" will be its only food supply. The plants often grow several feet from the shelter of the rocks, so it gathers them at the risk of being caught by a hawk or coyote. In its home somewhere deep under the rocks, only the marten and weasel are agile and small enough to find it.

In the security of these rocky retreats, female pikas have a single litter of three or four young in the spring. Where there are many of these little animals, their unused or abandoned hay piles gradually fill in the rock slides with fertile soil.

A second species of pika, the collared pika, *Ochotona collaris,* has a distinct grayish patch on its nape and shoulders. The collared pika ranges from southern Alaska through the southern part of Yukon Territory and the northwestern corner of British Columbia, into western Mackenzie Territory.

Colorado's Alpine Hay Cutter

In all its beauty, the alpine country of Colorado has an overpowering force about it. Every element is severe, potent, and frightening. The wind rarely ceases, and the earth's gravity, exaggerated by the steepness of the slopes, never ends its pull on the rock cliffs, slides, and soil. Persistent, too, is frost, which is present during much of the short growing season. The long bleak winters are masters of this zone, keeping most life dormant the greater part of the year.

Yet, in the face of all these odds, a small and delicate but robust mammal thrives, making its home in the loose rocks of the mountain sides. And though it is virtually unknown to the majority of people, it likes to give its call of curiosity to those few humans who do visit its habitat. This round, furry, rabbitlike inhabitant of the rocks is the pika, also commonly known as the cony.

Perhaps the most intriguing thing about the pika is its habitat—the formidable, barren-looking rock slides.

The pika sometimes lives in old decayed woodpiles but prefers rock slides

American Indians called the pika "little chief," giving rise to one of its present-day names, little chief hare. It is also called rock rabbit, whistling hare, and tailless rabbit. Although closely related to hares and rabbits, pikas more nearly resemble small gray guinea pigs. They have shorter ears than rabbits, shorter hind legs, and no visible tail. They are about eight inches long, buffy gray in color, and have very soft fur and ears. The whiskers are long and prominent. In between the small, black toe pads, there are numerous, stiff, white hairs that help to give it sure-footed traction on the rocks. In general appearance, the cony looks somewhat like a small chinchilla.

The young, which are usually born in early summer, are generally grayer in color than the adults. Later in the season they acquire a more tawny shade. Like the young of other mammals, young pikas are not as shy, as confident, nor as agile as the adults. On Fairview Peak in Colorado in July, young pikas have been observed together that were about four inches long and almost uniformly gray in color.

Pikas, or conies as they are called, live in loose colonies and each individual appears to have a small area that is its very own. The pika's home range is very small, about one-tenth of an acre, and is centered around its "haystack." In this area the pika has special rocks on which it sits, watches, and gives its call. During the course of a day, it will make its rounds about every hour, hopping up on these perches here and there, and then moving out of the area on a longer journey. These trips out of the pika's immediate home area occur quite regularly, even when it is not harvesting. During the winter it does not hibernate, but its activity is much less, because of the deep snow.

Although pikas live mainly in rock slides, they sometimes take up residence in old slab piles. In Comanche Gulch, Colorado, several pikas lived in a heap of decaying slabs. These conies had favorite perches among the slabs much the same as those inhabiting the rocks.

Voice of the pika is usually a one note call, although some conies give a call that has two notes close together. Sometimes the sound is a chatter that finally breaks into the single note. The typical call sounds somewhat like a nasal *eehk*, with a plaintive quality about it. In giving its call, a pika thrusts its head forward, and twitches its ears at the same time. Because pikas are hard to see, the best way to locate them is by their calls. At the approach of an intruder, almost every pika in the slide will burst out with calls of curiosity and warning.

The most admirable habit of the pika is its preparation for winter. In late summer it gathers a variety of green plants from the edges of the slide, cures them in the sun, and stores them under rocks within the slide. This is its "haypile." In some alpine areas, where vegetation is scant and dwarfed, it will cache almost any kind of green plant, i.e., lichens, mosses, willows, grasses, sedges, and forbs, which are herbaceous plants other than grasses. At more lush locations, it is more particular, harvesting only the plants that it especially likes. Usually the haypile of the new season is heaped upon the remains of the stack of the previous year.

The pika's method of gathering plants is amusing to watch. Where plants are small, it will get a good bite on the stem, just above the ground, and pull backward, tugging like a pup on a rag. When the stem or root gives way, it will scurry off with the morsel in its mouth. Where plants are larger, it cuts them with its teeth, and if the pieces are too long to carry, it drags them to its stack.

At Silverton, Colorado, during the harvest season, an observer baited a favorite pika perch with slices of apple. The pika nibbled the first slice and at once took it to its cache. It continued to carry away every slice of apple placed on the rock, but never again ate any above ground. Later, in November, it showed no interest in apples. There was snow on the slide at this time, and the

The short-tailed weasel is a frequent threat to the pika

pika was considerably less active than at harvest time.

The pika's preference for plants depends on where it lives and the plants that grow in the area. On Cannibal Mesa, Colorado, in the alpine meadows, pikas gathered mainly clover, sedges, kobresia, and rushes. On Cumberland Pass, where plants were dwarfed and sparse, the haypiles contained a wide assortment of plants, from lichens and mosses to thistles and willows. Just below timberline, in Comanche Gulch, pikas preferred bluebell, gentian, cinquefoil, elder, and various grasses and sedges.

During harvest time, pikas are very active, making many trips outside the slide. This is the time when a pika may be caught by hand, for it can be cornered on solid ground, behind a stump or rock. Trying to catch one among the loose rocks of the slide, however, would be very foolish, for the pika has infinite crevices among the rocks into which it can dive at the slightest hint of danger.

Close associates of the pika are various mice, ptarmigans, marmots, weasels, martens, and least chipmunks. In addition to the ptarmigan, a variety of songbirds frequent the slide and its edges. Eagles and some of the hawks prey on the pika, but their take is light. The main four-footed enemies of the pika are weasels and martens.

Although shy, the pika is curious. If one walks noisely to a spot where a pika has just disappeared, and stands, motionless, after five minutes of waiting, it will usually pop up, very cautiously, to get a look at the intruder. In trying to approach a visible pika, one might use a soft, squeaky whistle while walking slowly toward it. Its head will turn this way and that, which makes it appear to be occupied with the noise. It will disappear, quick as a wink, if one approaches it too closely.

As more people visit the high western mountains, more will get to know the pika. In addition to the many other fascinating features of the high country, they will find in the pika a charming creature that will help to make one's trips there more rewarding. (*See also Arctic-Alpine*) —T.E.

PIKE

The fishes known as pikes of the family Esocidae include the pickerels, which are known as the true pikes. All pickerels are in the genus *Esox,* which has representatives in northern Europe, in Asia, and in North America. Five species live in freshwater lakes, ponds, and streams of the United States and of these, three have been selected for discussion here. All have several physical characteristics that are typical of their genus. These characteristics (which will not be discussed under the individual fishes) include elongated, slender bodies and heads; very long jaws armed with large, sharp teeth; an absence of spines from all fins; one dorsal fin, which is located far back on the body.

The two pickerels not chosen for discussion are the grass pickerel, *Esox americanus vermiculatus,* and the redfin pickerel, *Esox americanus americanus.*

Chain Pickerel

Other Common Names—Eastern common pickerel, green pike
Scientific Name—*Esox niger*
Family—Esocidae (pikes)
Order—Clupeiformes
Size—Length, up to 25 inches
Range—Throughout eastern United States and slightly more westward in South

Chain pickerel more than 10 inches long have olive-green or yellow-green backs. Their sides are colored lightly and have dark, irregular, chain-shaped markings. The belly is milky white, often tinged with yellow. A dark line runs down vertically from the lower part of the eye and is appropriately called a "teardrop." Young chain pickerels under 8 or 10 inches do not have the typical

Chain pickerel

Muskellunge

Northern pike

chain-shaped markings. Instead, they are barred and mottled darkly (*See also under Fish: Common Freshwater Fishes of North America*).

Muskellunge
Other Common Names—Maskinonge, musky, tiger musky, leopard musky
Scientific Name—*Esox masquinongy*
Family—Esocidae (pikes)
Order—Clupeiformes
Size—Length, up to about 50 inches
Range—In and around the Great Lakes and the states bordering them

The coloring of a muskellunge varies widely. Usually fishes more than a foot long have olive-green, yellowish-olive or brownish-olive backs. Their sides are lighter, usually yellow-green to gray, with dusky vertical rows of spots, bars, or blotches. The belly is white or yellowish. Smaller muskellunges often have yellow-green backs, lighter sides banded with oblique olive-green bars, and a white belly.

The muskellunge eats a wide variety of fishes and also many frogs, crayfishes, and insects. Muskellunges have also been known to attack and eat ducklings and other birds and even small mammals. Because of their size, (individuals up to 40 pounds are not uncommon) wariness, and fighting qualities, they are one of the most sought after of game fish.

Northern Pike
Other Common Names—Pickerel, jackfish, common pike, snake, great northern pike
Scientific Name—*Esox lucius*
Family—Esocidae (pikes)
Order—Clupeiformes
Size—Length, up to 4 feet
Range—Throughout North America north of the Ohio River. Also widely distributed in northern Europe

Northern pikes show great variation in color. Their backs and sides may be green to olive-brown. The sides are marked with small white or yellowish spots. The belly is yellowish-white. Young ones may have oblique bars instead of these spots.

The northern pike eats mostly other fishes and many insects. It may attack and eat young ducks swimming about on the surfaces of streams and ponds, also other small waterbirds. Because it is a good fighter when hooked, it is a popular game fish. —M.R.

PINE

The Pinaceae, the pine family, contains pines, larches, spruces, firs, and hemlocks in one tribe, bald cypress in another, and white cedar, arborvitae, and the junipers in a third.

Within that group, the pines are classified together under the genus name

The tightly sealed green cones of pitch pine (above) open when ripe to release their winged seeds (below)

The cones of pines vary greatly in size and form and are a sure guide to the identification of these coniferous trees

1. *Scotch pine* (Pinus sylvestris)
2. *Red pine* (Pinus resinosa)
3. *White pine* (Pinus strobus)
4. *Himalayan pine* (Pinus griffithii)
5. *Mountain pine* (Pinus mugo)
6. *Pitch pine* (Pinus rigida)
7. *Austrian pine* (Pinus nigra)

Pinus. There are about 90 species of pine in North America. Most of them are tall, with the ponderosa pine of the West at times reaching 200 feet. The most widely distributed pine is the western yellow pine, that grows from British Columbia to Texas.

Pines are extremely ancient in comparison with the hardwoods, or flowering trees. They appeared in the Pennsylvanian Period, about 300 million years ago, and flourished during the Mesozoic Era. The angiosperms, or flowering plants, did not evolve until the Cretaceous Period, some 165 million years later. Since then they have usurped the former dominance of the gymnosperms, the older group to which the pines belong.

Everyone should be able to tell a pine tree at sight, because all pines have long green needles. These needles are really the leaves of the tree. Also, the needles are in bundles, called fascicles, and each fascicle usually contains a definite number of needles.

The pines are a group of conifers or cone-bearing trees, and one of the best ways to determine the species is to examine one of its cones. A cone is composed of more or less thick woody scales arranged in a spiral fashion around a central axis. Each cone-scale bears at its base two exposed, or naked, seeds. Before the cone is ready to discharge its seeds it is closed.

A system of tiny canals carrying resin

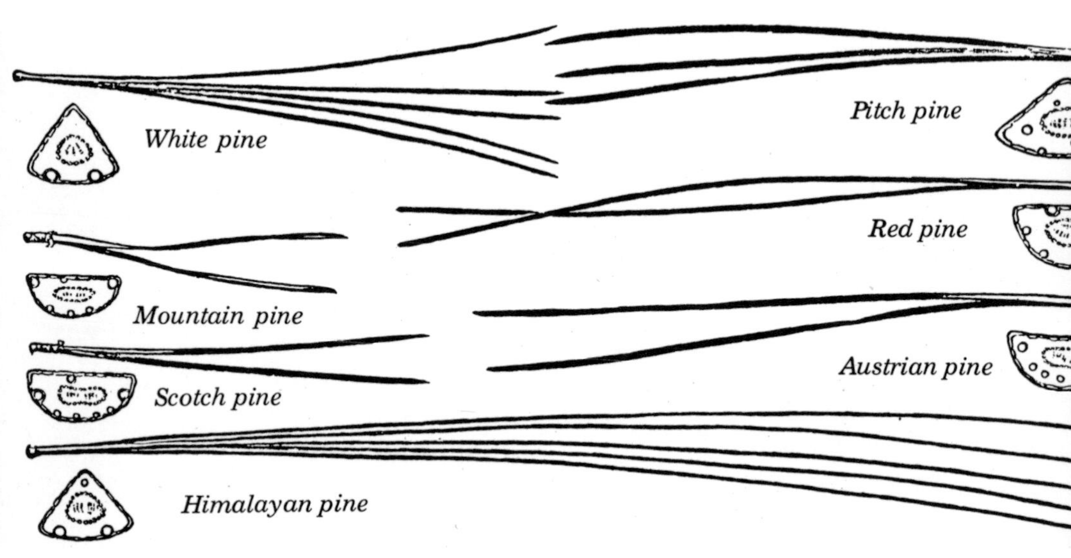

The placement of resin ducts through pine needles varies with the species

traverses the tree lengthwise and crosswise, so that one cannot cut into a twig, or slice off the bark without cutting into one or more of these resin ducts, just as one cannot cut one's finger without severing one or more of the tiny tubes or vessels through which the blood circulates. The resin is valuable to the tree itself, because it covers wounds and hardens, preventing dangerous fungi and insects from entering into the exposed tissues. And to man it is also valuable in many ways because from it is distilled turpentine, an important ingredient of paints. Large quantities of resin are collected from the southern pines, particularly from the longleaf pine, by gashing the trunks each year and catching the resin in containers. The residue, after the turpentine is distilled, is rosin, which has many more uses than furnishing a gripping surface for violin bows. Rosin is used in the making of sealing wax, soap, the glaze on paper, and for salve.

The resin duct system of a pine continues even into the leaves, one or more of these ducts extending lengthwise into the leaf; and the number and position of these ducts in the leaf is helpful in determining the species.

Usually toward the end of its second year, in the winter or early spring, the scales of the cone separate, exposing the naked seeds. Each seed is furnished (in most pines) with a broad but thin "wing," so that when it drops out of the cone on the tree it spins around in the air as it falls to the ground. The spinning takes time, and time is of extreme importance, for the longer the time that the seed takes to reach the ground, the greater is the chance that it will be caught up by a gust of wind and whirled off to some place more or less distant from the parent tree, where it can have more room to grow.

There the seed lies, perhaps on the snow, or on the frozen soil, amidst dead grass or fallen leaves, until the warm April sun starts the growth processes, especially those in the tiny embryo. First the seed absorbs some of the surrounding water, and its seed coat, now too small for it, bursts, and a tiny rootlet, or *hypocotyl,* is pushed down through the cracked seed coat into the moist, warm soil. There it establishes itself by fine branching rootlets, and then, growing faster toward the upper end, pushes off the seed coat surrounding its seed leaves, or cotyledons.

After the seed coat is sloughed off, a succession of long and single needle-shaped leaves, the primary leaves, is produced, above the cotyledons. These primary leaves become shorter and shorter as the season advances, until finally they are so small and crowded together as to form a fairly dense cluster at the tip of the stem. This is really the first terminal bud of the future pine tree.

The following spring this bud unfolds, and there is a change in appearance. Tiny buds which were at the base of the uppermost primary leaves unfold and give rise to the fascicles of secondary leaves. From now on the primary leaves are only small, brownish scales, the bud scales, of the winter buds, each one covering a tiny bud which includes a fascicle of secondary leaves. These secondary leaves are really leaves of tiny branches which never develop further, but drop off at the end of their second year or sometimes later; that is, the fascicles of leaves drop off and with the fascicles the tiny branches that bore them. But in the cedar (*Cedrus*) and the larch (*Larix*), trees closely related to the pine, these short branches continue

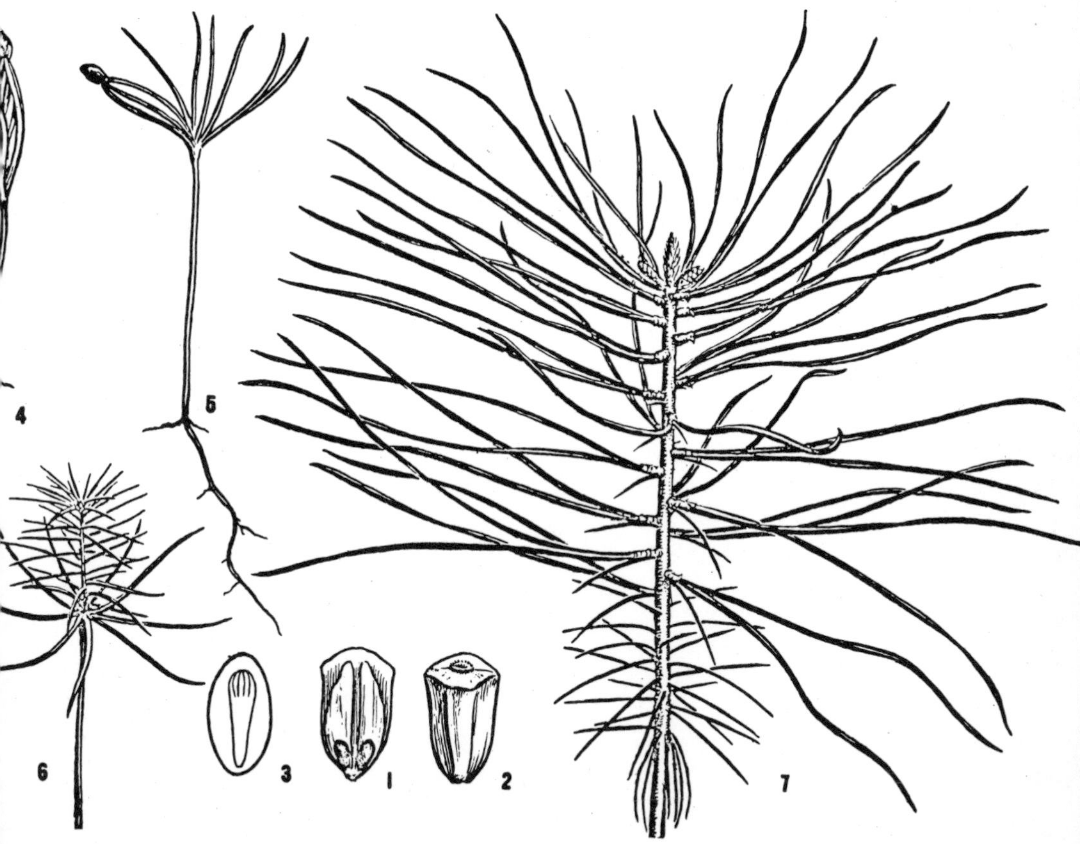

The development of a pine seedling begins with a winged seed (1); that is attached to a cone scale (2); the seed shown in cross-section (3); develops into a young seedling (4 and 5). Toward the end of the first year the primary leaves develop above the cotyledons (6). A two year old seedling (7) has well developed needles and leaf buds

growing year after year, bearing a cluster of leaves each year. These leaves are also in fascicles, but there is no definite number of leaves in a fascicle, as in the pine.

Most of the pines form a cluster of winter buds each year at the tip of the stem. The next year when these buds unfold, one of these, usually the central and largest, continues the erect growth of the tree while the others form a whorl or ring of branches. Thus the age of a pine can be easily told by counting the number of these rings or whorls of branches. Also, the rate at which the tree grows in different years can be easily seen.

Bristlecone Pine
Other Common Names—None
Scientific Name—*Pinus aristata*
Family—Pinaceae (pine family)
Range—Mountain ranges of the desert between the Rocky Mountains and the Sierra Nevada
Habitat—Exposed slopes, ridge tops often at upper limit of tree growth
Leaves—In bundles of five, 1 to 1½ inches long, stout and usually curved, dark green and shining on the back (upper surface), marked on the lower by several rows of whitish stomata, usually crowded on the ends of the twigs and appearing brushed forward and commonly with sticky white exudations of resin
Bark—On old trunks, red-brown and shallowly furrowed and ridged. Twigs stout, light orange becoming nearly black, bearing long tufts of foliage at the tips
Flowers—Male, dark orange-red; female, purple
Fruit—Cones 3 to 3½ inches long, short-stalked with thick scales dark chocolate-brown at ends, umbo with long, fragile, bristlelike prickle; often coated with exudations of shiny brown resin

About the year A.D. 768 when Charlemagne was crowned King of the Franks, a bristlecone pine, *Pinus aristata,* first started to grow in the far-off wilderness of America. By the time Columbus first sighted the Bahamas, the pine was a giant tree in the prime of life, with a massive trunk and thick, ascending branches. With the signing of the Declaration of Independence, this venerable tree had passed its one-thousandth birthday. Today it is a staunch but ragged veteran that has battled the elements for 12 centuries. Just how much more remains of its allotted life span, no one knows.

This particular bristlecone pine, which stands at an elevation of 10,285 feet atop Spectra Point on the edge of southern Utah's spectacular and color-splashed Cedar Breaks, is estimated by National Park Service naturalists to be 1,200 years old. In 32 years of observation, the tree has shown no changes whatever, except for the withering of a tiny green sprig at the tip of one of its branches. At that rate, this ancient pine will probably continue to exist for hundreds of years more before the last spark of life is extinguished.

But this bristlecone pine is a youngster compared to those in California's White Mountains. There, several gnarled patriarchs have been found to be over 4,000 years old. More ancient than the famed sequoias, they are the earth's oldest living things. The tree at Cedar Breaks can never compete with them in antiquity, for bristlecone pines live longer in the western part of their range than in the eastern. The reason, apparently, is that with less precipitation the trees grow much more slowly.

The bristlecone pines grow on the high mountain ranges in the great desert land between the Rockies and the Sierra Nevada. No trees thrive better at great heights, and they often occupy the most exposed slopes and ridge tops.

Buffeted by gales and racked by winter storms, the bristlecones show the results of their hard life in their twisted shapes, contorted branches and sand-blasted trunks. But they are tough, spartan trees, and prosper on adversity.

—W.H.

Bristlecone pin

Longleaf pine

Longleaf Pine
Other Common Names—Southern yellow pine, long-straw pine
Scientific Name—*Pinus australis*
Family—Pinaceae (pine family)
Range—Extreme southeastern Virginia, south through most of Florida, and west into eastern Texas
Habitat—Usually a tree of well-watered sandy soils forming coastal plain flatwoods but reaching to the Blue Ridge Mountains
Leaves—Rather slender, springy needles 8 to 18 inches long, borne in groups of 3 with a long, silky brown sheath. Bright green and tufted
Bark—Flaky, yellowish or lavender-gray with some orange-brown tones
Flowers—Male: light purplish catkins clustered around the new shoots, in early spring. The darker female blossoms appear a bit later and higher up on the tree
Fruit—The rugged cones are 6 to 10 inches long, with a short prickle on each lumpy scale

Like the pitch pines of the Middle Atlantic States, the longleaf pine is chiefly associated with sandy lowlands approaching the shore but it also has adapted itself to favorable soils in upland regions where the climate is not too severe. This is particularly true in Alabama where the Appalachian highlands terminate in a complex series of hills, valleys, upland plains, and ridges intersected by the tributaries of several Gulf rivers. Extending southward into peninsular Florida, the longleaf pine is gradually supplanted by slash pine—a similar species of West Indian origin.

The longleaf pine can be recognized from a distance by the length of its rather soft, long needles that are pliable and bend in graceful curves away from the center of the clumps on the ends of the twigs. In between this outer foliage and the trunk there is very little foliage, and only near the top of the plant does the vegetation form any great density.

Older longleaf pines are apt to develop an irregular rather flat massing of the foliage high on the straight, towering trunks that used to be cut for masts and spars in the days when these trees were used to supply the shipbuilding industry. The wood of the longleaf pine, generally known as yellow pine, or southern yellow pine, is used for heavy construction, ties, flooring, and special finishing work. It is hard, strong, and durable and like many abundant trees, it has suffered from overcutting as well as from forest fires.

Another product of longleaf pine use and that of several other southern species (notably slash pine) is turpentine, rosin, and related products made from the resin of these trees. A V-shaped cut is made in the bark of the trunk, and the fluids are collected in a cup or box. The cut wood is also boiled out or steamdistilled for similar purposes. Although tapping for turpentine does not severely affect or kill the trees when properly done, it naturally places some drain on the plants' vitality.

Turpentining is so widely practiced that the typical inverted-chevron cut appears on a large proportion of the trees in many southern pine forests. —M.H.B.

Pinyon Pine
Other Common Names—Nut pine, Colorado pinyon pine
Scientific Name—*Pinus edulis*
Family—Pinaceae (pine family)
Range—Southern Rocky Mountain region of Utah, Colorado, Arizona, and New Mexico
Habitat—Semiarid regions, poor sites at intermediate elevations
Leaves—Needles arranged 2 or 3 in a cluster, ¾ to 1½ inches in length, dark green
Bark—Reddish-brown and furrowed in scaly ridges
Flower—Typical pine blossoms
Fruit—Small egg-shaped cones, 1½ to 2 inches long, with stout, blunt scales, and large wingless, edible seeds

Pinyon pine (foreground) often grows in association with juniper (rear)

Of the various kinds of pinyon pine that grow in different areas or elevations in the Southwest the common, or two-leafed, pinyon, *Pinus edulis*, is especially representative. As in the case with several Atlantic Coastal pines, it can grow successfully in the poorest soils, often occurring on old lava flows, but attains a greater luxuriance and large size with more water and better nourishment. Only slightly less tolerant of severe weather conditions than the western junipers it can tolerate temperatures as high as 110° and as low as 25° below zero and will survive on less than 13 inches of annual rainfall. While often growing with other trees such as ponderosa pine, oak, and various shrublike species it may form pure stands on moist, flat ground where its form becomes much like that of such eastern species as pitch pine. The maximum height is about 50 feet but the average size is well below that.

The pinyons are slow-growing trees at best, and their wood is rather soft. They have been used for such purposes as fencing, poles, mine timbers, and others. By far the more general use of the tree is for its "nuts" which are actually the seeds that develop in the ripened cones. Some of the cones, imperfectly fertilized in their youth, may contain two or three seeds, others, a couple of dozen. Whole trees have been known to yield several

Pitch pine (left); shortleaf pine (right)

bushels of nuts each and the collection, roasting, and sale of these can be a fairly profitable small business. Most of these are sold in the West but these trees will survive in our eastern states where they are sometimes planted as ornamentals on private grounds. —M.H.B.

Pitch Pine
Other Common Names—Southern yellow pine
Scientific Name—*Pinus rigida*
Family—Pinaceae (pine family)
Range—Maine and eastern Ontario, western New York, northeastern Pennsylvania, and eastern Ohio south to Virginia, and mountains of Georgia, Kentucky, and Tennessee
Habitat—Sandy or barren soils, often near the shore or in mountainous areas
Leaves—Needles three to six inches long, stiff, slightly twisted and growing in groups of three
Bark—Very rough and flaky showing much lavender-gray and dark brown
Flowers—Typical pine blossoms appearing in early spring
Fruit—Broad, prickly cones two to three inches long, usually in pairs, remaining on the tree for several seasons

Pitch pine grows in such a variety of habitats and locations that it is hard to make valid generalizations about it. Rugged, even rocky, mountaintops are not excluded as sites for its establishment and it appears with Virginia pine in the Transition Zone between northern deciduous woods and the southeastern coniferous forests. Typically, however, it is a pine barrens tree, the predominant species in those sandy-gravelly soils near the shore, forming extensive forested plains interrupted only by scrub oak and an undergrowth of laurel and other low-growing species and by the white cedar swamps that surround the waterways.

The size and shape of the pitch pine is as varied as its habitats. Often, where a subsurface hardpan dwarfs the root system, it is a scrub tree, sometimes only 8 or 10 feet tall with lower branches sweeping the ground. In deeper sands and clay it may attain considerable size (up to 100 feet or so) and in wet areas of the South, beginning as far north as Cape May, New Jersey, a variety called pond pine, *P. rigida serotina*, occurs.

In any place or form in which it appears, pitch pine is an "informal," tree, seldom attaining its maximum size because of the soil condition in which it so often grows, but always stubborn and vital, springing up or sprouting from stumps, even after quite severe fires. Whether on a mountaintop behind New

England beaches, or on the coastal plain of New Jersey it is a noticeable and subtly attractive species, easily recognized even at a distance by the pairs of cones that remain on the tree after they are open, sometimes for several years. By this feature it may be quickly separated from the little-coned shortleaf pine with which it often occurs.

In the extreme northeastern and north-central states there is a tree somewhat equivalent to pitch pine in its ability to accommodate to semisterile, sandy soils —this is the jack pine, *P. banksiana*, which in degree resembles the former species in bark and general form. Neither of these trees is heavily used for lumber because of irregular growth and small size but both are cut for pulpwood and fuel. As with many species, they are both of great value in foresting and holding soils in which few other trees can grow.

—M.H.B.

Ponderosa Pine
Other Common Names—Western yellow pine, Arizona pine
Scientific Name—*Pinus ponderosa*
Family—Pinaceae (pine family)
Range—At moderate elevations in the Cascade Range, from British Columbia and Washington to San Francisco; down the Sierra Nevada into Baja California and on the southern California coast; also throughout most of the Rocky Mountain plateau, into Nebraska and western Texas; south into the highlands of Mexico
Habitat—Mountain slopes and plateaus in all but the most inhospitable conditions
Leaves—Rather stiff needles, 5 to 10 inches long, in bundles of 2 or 3
Bark—Brown to black and furrowed even on young trees; yellowish-brown or cinnamon-red and broken into large, flat, scaly plates with great cracks on slow-growing older trunks
Flowers—Typical reddish female "conelets" and yellowish male "candles"
Fruit—The cones are about four inches (three to six inches) long, with thickened scales, each bearing a recurved bristle

Ponderosa and its near relative the Jeffrey pine have together a very wide range that includes almost all the mountainous areas of the western states excluding only the very damp north Pacific margin. In the Rocky Mountains, the Arizona plateaus and through much of northern California the ponderosa predominates, adapting itself to different soil and weather conditions that produce considerable variety in its appearance. In some areas it may grow to 230 feet in height with 6- to 8-foot trunk diameters. Younger trees, much smaller than this, have a flat, scaly bark cracked into broad pinkish or yellow brown plates that make it resemble the southeastern shortleaf, but on old trees the cracks become so broad and the bark so dark it is sometimes called blackjack pine. A further resemblance to shortleaf pine is in the fact that the needles may be borne in twos or threes, although they are much longer (5 to 10 inches).

Jeffrey pine has a narrower range, limited generally to the drier eastern slopes of the Sierra Nevada and the mountains of southern California, plus a few restricted areas in Oregon. It is characterized by a bluish color of foliage, a frequently darker bark, and by very large, beehive-shaped cones up to 15 inches long (ponderosa cones rarely exceed 6 inches or so). These often litter the needle-strewn open ground under the trees and their seeds, like those of many conifers, supply considerable food for mice, squirrels, and some birds.

Both of these trees are called western yellow pine in the lumber trade. The light-colored sapwood much resembles white pine while the darker inner cuts are of harder, stronger quality that suit them for moderately heavy structural use. Very large quantities are cut annually and it is only through replanting and diligent forestry practices that the

Western yellow pine

supply is able to keep up with the demand. Fires in the western coniferous forests, particularly on slopes and mountains, can be fierce and devastating, consuming the tops and the whole of trees—not just low-level brush. In addition to such calamities as these there are several insect diseases and parasites to which ponderosa (and Jeffrey) pine is subjected, a fact that does not make it any easier to insure the growth of healthy new forests.

One hopes that whatever chemical control measures are used in trying to combat these problems they will not adversely affect the wild animal life and birdlife of such regions. Many of them are extremely beautiful, particularly in some of the highlands of Arizona where the ground at certain seasons is carpeted with flowers and there is much open parklike woodland—a startling contrast to the stark and arid valleys a few thousand feet below. —M.H.B.

Red Pine
Other Common Names—Norway pine
Scientific Name—*Pinus resinosa*
Family—Pinaceae (pine family)
Range—From Nova Scotia, southern Quebec, to southeastern Manitoba; Maine to Minnesota (except southern portions); south to Connecticut, northern New Jersey, and northeastern Pennsylvania (away from coastal plain)
Habitat—Dry woods, especially in the Great Lakes region where it grows abundantly in sandy plains
Leaves—Needles in pairs, usually five to six inches long, dark yellow-green, moderately slender with a noticeable, persistent sheath. When bent double, red pine needles snap crisply
Bark—Clay-red or orange-cinnamon and flaky when young; developing into large, flat reddish-brown plates, roughly diamond-shaped and irregularly fissured
Flowers—Clusters of purple, pollen-bearing male blossoms, each about one-half inch long appear along the new twigs in May or June; the stubby, scarlet female flowers come in pairs higher up on the tree
Fruit—Cones, single or in pairs, about two inches long without sharp prickles, borne close to the stem; often partly hidden among the needles

For the beginner in tree study, red pine may be one of the harder trees to identify unless he or she is already familiar with it. The species has various traits suggestive of other pines but no characteristics of appearance that are infallibly outstanding. The bark, although suggestive of some of the southern pines, is apt to be finer-grained and of a more purplish red color on younger and upper trunks, and of course it is a northern species whose natural range does not much overlap that of southeastern trees. Still, there is considerable resemblance between the foliage of red and longleaf pines, particularly in dense stands of rather young growth, a superficial similarity that can be checked by looking at the number of needles in a "bundle" (the red pine has two, the longleaf three) and by noting the crisp way the red pine needles snap when bent double. The general shape and size of the cones is not too helpful because several trees that may occur in parts of the red pine's range also have small cones under two inches long.

The wood of red pine has qualities intermediate between soft white pine and the hard, strong, resinous longleaf lumber, and is moderately heavy and has a wide variety of uses. The tree is, generally speaking, not as abundant as many other pines but considerable quantities are cut in the region of the Great Lakes. It reproduces quite rapidly after forest fires and grows at a good rate when young if it has sufficient sunlight. Red pine is capable of growing a foot a year, slowing down gradually afterward. The average height of a good stand of mature trees averages close to 100 feet while the maximum is about 140 feet, with trunks up to 4 or 5 feet in diameter. —M.H.B.

Red pine

Shortleaf Pine
Other Common Names—Yellow pine, long-tag pine
Scientific Name—*Pinus echinata*
Family—Pinaceae (pine family)
Range—Northern Florida to northeastern Texas, north in eastern United States to West Virginia, New Jersey, and southeastern New York. West to southern Ohio, southern Idaho, southern Missouri, and eastern Oklahoma
Habitat—Usually dry or sandy soils
Leaves—Slender needles, 2½ to 5 inches long, dark blue-green, 2 or 3 in a cluster
Bark—Reddish-brown, with large irregular, flat, scaly plates
Flower—Typical pine blossoms
Fruit—Small cones, 1½ to 2½ inches long, dull brown, with small prickles

Shortleaf pine can usually be distinguished from pitch pine even at a fair distance by its broader, more regular shape, reddish-brown bark and smaller clumps of foliage forming a rather rounded crown at the top of the tree. Its longer branches spring straight out from a solid-looking trunk, the lower ones sloping gently downward, and the small cones often grow singly rather than in pairs. Only in forests where they may grow close together and the upper foliage cannot be clearly seen is there much difficulty identifying pitch and shortleaf pine.

The shortleaf pine is fairly large, with a maximum height near to 120 feet and a trunk diameter up to about 4 feet. Such large trees are more apt to be found in the interior southern part of its range—it is not primarily a lower coastal plain species as are several other southeastern spines. In the states bordering the Mississippi river basin it is abundant and is plentiful even into eastern Texas and Oklahoma. It is cut extensively for lumber. About one-third of commercially sold southern pine is estimated to be of this species. The wood, known also as yellow pine, or Carolina pine, is lighter in weight and not quite as hard and resinous as that of the longleaf. Although it occurs in the same general areas of the upland south, shortleaf seems to grow best in dry woods and somewhat richer soils, while longleaf pine grows well in less fertile situations. —M.H.B.

Sugar Pine
Other Common Names—California sugar pine
Scientific Name—*Pinus lambertiana*
Family—Pinaceae (pine family)
Range—Western Oregon and northern California and southward in the Sierra Nevada and higher mountains to central California
Habitat—Western mountain slopes and canyons where there is ample annual rainfall
Leaves—Borne in groups of five usually three to four inches long and thick, with

Mature sugar pines attain heights of 250 feet with trunk diameters of 16 or more feet

Sugar pine cones are larger than those of any other cone-bearing tree

a deep blue-green color (yellower when new), often silvery

Bark—Smooth and gray when young, becoming reddish as it splits with age, finally rough cinnamon or purplish-brown. Often marked by encrusted drippings of the pleasantly sweet, white resin

Flower—Typical male and female pine blossoms, the latter developing quite long stems

Fruit—Hanging cones 10 to 20 inches long (purple-green and cigar-shaped before opening), often covered with abundant droplets or resin

Sugar pine is the classic giant western pine, a tree of solid proportions with a massive trunk when fully grown, and the largest cones of any pine. These are as much as 21 inches long and 3 or 4 inches in diameter while the maximum height of the trees is near 250 feet with trunk diameters of 16 feet or more. These trees are "companions in gianthood" to the redwoods and the Douglas-firs.

The bulk of sugar pine found today is in the largely uninhabited region bridging southwestern Oregon and northern California, but it's range extends southward in a spotty fashion into the mountains of southern California and the Coast Ranges. Although poorer soils and less rainfall may "starve" the tree in some areas a typically healthy sugar pine growing in favorable conditions is an impressive and picturesque sight. The thick tufts of fine needles clumping at the upturned ends of quite stout branches give the tree a solid, well-clothed appearance lacking in some of the other white pines. The downswept lowest branches often break off leaving dried or mossy stumps that seem more a testimony to the great trees sustaining strength than a sign of weakness or injury, but like other members of this group of pines any break in the bark is followed by a crystaline-white gum oozing out and dripping down the trunk. In this species these pitchy, resinous exudations are sometimes picked off and chewed because of their rather sweet flavor—hence the name sugar pine.

The winged seeds that fall from the giant cones when they open have an "edible kernel about the size of a grain of corn which is relished by many birds and animals." Because of the artistic form of the branches and foliage, many films on wildlife in forested California locations frequently picture this tree, and it has come to almost typify Pacific Coastal scenes in the minds of many who have never visited there—a tree that one expects might harbor a pair of bear cubs or a mountain lion. And probably sugar pines often do if they are not of an age or size to virtually defy climbing.

Requiring upwards of forty inches of annual rainfall for healthy development and occurring up to considerable altitudes where snowfall may account for most of this, the sugar pine is a beautiful sight in winter, laden with snow that accumulates to a depth of many feet.

Like all the white pines it is subject to a disease called white pine blister rust which has, as part of its life cycle, the currant and gooseberry bushes for an intermediate host. Because of the value of its excellent wood, second only to eastern white pine in fine quality, texture, and "workability," private and government agencies have gone to some lengths to eliminate this tree disease by attempting to destroy all berry bushes in the area of large sugar pine forests.

—M.H.B.

White Pine

Other Common Names—Eastern white pine, northern pine

Scientific Name—*Pinus strobus*

Family—Pinaceae (pine family)

Range—From Newfoundland, southern Quebec and Ontario to southeastern Manitoba; Maine to Minnesota, south to eastern Iowa, northern Illinois, and Indiana, and in the highlands to northern Georgia

Habitat—Woodlands, especially in the Northeast

Leaves—Slender, soft needles 2½ to 5 inches long, borne in groups of 5. Bright green when new, they usually become much darker, and each needle has a faint pale stripe which may give the massed foliage a bluish cast

Bark—Smooth and slate-gray or olive when young, but sometimes with a reddish or bronze tone. Soon splits and forms a rough, gravelly or scaly gray surface with irregular vertical grooves. Usually marked with white streaks of dripping pine gum

Flower—Pollen-filled male blossoms are clustered around new growth on the lower branches; and small, pink female ones are high on the tree and appear in May or June

Fruit—Distinctive hanging cones, green and cigar-shaped during growth, becoming 4 to 10 inches long by the time they mature in their second season and fall to the ground. Seeds with a long, thin papery wing

Of all the eastern trees that first settlers encountered, the tallest by far were the huge white pines that stood above the surrounding deciduous forest. To a degree they were holdovers from an earlier age of predominantly coniferous forest—in size, rivals of their western cousins on the Pacific Coast. By no small misfortune all of these were eventually cut down. Now an eastern white pine a yard in diameter and 125 feet high is considered a veritable giant.

Wherever large trees of this species occur and can be seen from a distance they may almost instantly be recognized by their flat, separated masses of foliage with upreaching tips, that appear dark blue-green or almost black against the sky. Often the treetops are flat, too, for white pine is a fast-growing, rather weak wood and the terminal branches are apt to be broken off by ice or storm by the time they have grown above the level of the surrounding trees. This form is quite in contrast to their rather conical shape when young.

Another outstanding characteristic of white pine is the soft, fine needles, each bearing a pale whitish stripe which gives the bluish tinge to the foliage. Occasionally one sees white pines with shorter needles than most, and of a rather pale, yellow-green. When this is consistent it may be regarded as subspecific, or racial, in character, for even though it is essentially a northeastern tree, it grows in quite a wide variety of soils and climate, from northern Georgia to Canada's Laurentian uplands. These habitat variations tend to produce local differences in the appearance of the tree. Wherever it occurs, however, there is almost no tree that can be confused with it after even cursory observation. The cigar-shaped cones that spring open upon drying, and the rather smooth trunks that drip white gum wherever it is bruised or a branch is broken are quick marks of identification. The delicate, five-needled foliage that sighs softly in the slightest breeze and the somber, cool effect of the older trees also characterize the whole "mood" of the white pine. Whether prized for the excellent, workable quality of its rather soft wood, or for its value as a windbreak or as a decorative tree, this is an important and attractive species.

—M.H.B.

White pine

PINE, GROUND (*See under Club Mosses and Horsetails*)

PINE SISKIN
Other Common Names—Pine finch, pine linnet
Scientific Name—*Spinus pinus*
Family—Fringillidae (grosbeaks, finches, sparrows, and buntings)
Order—Passeriformes
Size—Length, 4¾ inches
Range—From limit of tree growth in Canada south in central United States, northern Wisconsin, central Michigan, Kansas, Iowa and east to northern Pennsylvania, southeastern New York, and Connecticut. South to Florida, the Gulf Coast, Baja California, and, in winter, to northeastern Mexico

Like the redpoll, the pine siskin is one of those widely distributed birds whose movements depend, to a great extent, upon the weather and the food supply (*See Redpoll*). Some years it is absent from much of the region south of its breeding range; in other years it is abundant there. The nest is built in coniferous trees and is made of rootlets and grasses and lined with pine needles and hair. The eggs are from three to four, greenish-white, and speckled with reddish-brown.

Pine siskin

PINNIPED (*See Sea Lions and Seals; and under Walrus*)

PINTAIL
Other Common Names—Harlan, long-necked cracker, splittail
Scientific Name—*Anas acuta*
Family—Anatidae (swans, geese, and ducks)
Order—Anseriformes
Size—Length, 26 to 30 inches
Range—Breeds chiefly in western North America, from northwestern Alaska and northern Mackenzie, east to Quebec and New Brunswick, and south to southern California, northern Arizona, Colorado, Nebraska, Iowa, Illinois, and casually east to northern Pennsylvania. Winters along the Pacific Coast from Alaska to Central America, and from northeastern Colorado, Oklahoma, southern Illinois, southern Ohio, and Massachusetts to the West Indies

Among the very first ducks to push northward in the spring are the pintails. Their long, thin necks, slender bodies, and needle-pointed tails make them the most streamlined of all the wild ducks. Their larger relatives, the geese, fly in wedges, one bird partly behind the other. The pintails fly breast to breast in a curving line. They travel high, and when they spot an ice-free pool in the marsh, they set their wings and drop like meteors, twisting this way and that to check their headlong rush.

The male pintails sport white breasts and a white streak on either side of their brown heads. Their long, pointed tails are held clear of the water and help identify them from the other surface-feeding ducks. The females are brown, not particularly distinctive, and rather difficult to tell from other species of female ducks.

Perhaps no other duck in the world, except the mallard, is so widely known (*See Mallard*). In most of the East, pintails are present only in winter or in migration; but where little lakes dot the western prairies, or marshy pools are formed in the cool arctic tundra, they find their summer homes. Here they no longer travel in flocks, but are found in pairs not far apart.

Most waterfowl nest in wet spots in marshes—soggy places where the newly-hatched young can get to the water quickly. The pintail's nest, however, is almost always placed where it is dry. It might be on an island, or as much as half a mile from any water in the dry prairie. Sometimes the nest is in clear view, without much straw or grass to hide it. There are between 5 and 12 eggs (usually less than 10) resting on a soft bed of down plucked from the female's breast. When she leaves the nest, this soft woolly down is quickly pulled over the eggs to hide them from sharp-eyed predators. The brown female incubates the eggs for 22 or 23 days while her mate withdraws a short distance away. After the young have hatched, he often helps in their care. As the eggs are laid one each day, they would hatch a day apart if they were incubated right from the start. The female prevents this by waiting until all the eggs are laid before she begins brooding them. The entire brood then hatches within a few hours of each other.

The fuzzy young stay in the nest for a day or two until they are well dried; then they leave, toddling in a little compact group across the dry prairie after their mother. It is sometimes quite a long walk to water.

They are grayer than most other young

Pintail, male (foreground); female (rear)

ducks, light below and dark above, with a black line through the eye. In three weeks feathers begin to show. In a short time they can fly. At about the same time their parents temporarily lose their own ability to fly because of molting. Most ducks molt their long wing feathers in July, which makes flight impossible.

Pintails do not dive for their food as some of the other ducks do, but tip up for it, paddling their feet for balance while they stretch their long necks down to the muddy bottom for the bulblets, roots, and seeds of water plants. Seven-eighths of the pintail's food is made up of such vegetable matter as pondweeds, sedges, duckweeds, and algae. The rest is mostly insects, minnows, worms, tadpoles, and other animal life found in the water. —A.B., Jr.

PIPIT

Water Pipit

Other Common Names—American pipit, prairie titlark

Scientific Name—*Anthus spinoletta*

Family—Motacillidae (wagtails and pipits)

Order—Passeriformes

Size—Length, 6¼ inches

Range—Breeds in Arctic from northeastern Siberia, northern Alaska and west coast of Greenland south to Great Slave Lake, northern Quebec and Newfoundland, and on high mountains south to Colorado and New Mexico. Winters from southern California, and the Ohio and Delaware valleys south to the Gulf Coast and Guatemala

Water pipit

The water pipit is a bird of the open windswept skies and of the fields and prairies. Nesting mostly beyond the haunts of man, our chief acquaintance with pipits is during their winter sojourn and the period of their migratory movements. Often in late autumn or early spring, their faint and plaintive *dee-dee-dee* may be heard far overhead, as with billowy, airy flight they go trailing across the sky. They travel in loose flocks and light gracefully in the fields or pastures, where they scatter irregularly to feed. They are particularly fond of plowed fields, and, in farming districts, they are most often seen there.

They are terrestrial in their habits and rarely light in trees. They walk and run gracefully and their habit of tail-wagging affords a ready means of distinguishing them from shore larks whose flight and haunts are similar.

The nest is on the ground, and of grasses. From four to six bluish-white eggs, thickly speckled with cinnamon-brown, are laid.

Sprague's pipit, *Anthus spragueii,* is lighter in color, with yellow legs, a lighter bill, and brown stripes of buff on the back. It has the same tail pattern of white edges but the breast is lighter with less streaking.

A bird of the northern plains, Sprague's pipit breeds from Saskatchewan to northwestern Minnesota, and migrates in winter to the Gulf Coast.

PITCHER PLANT

Other Common Names—Huntsman's cup, sidesaddle flower

Scientific Name—*Sarracenia purpurea*

Family—Sarraceniaceae (pitcher plant family)

Order—Sarraceniales

Size—To 2½ feet tall

Range—Labrador to Mackenzie River, south to Great Lakes, Iowa, and Florida

The leaves of this unusual plant form open-ended tubes that fill with rainwater. Both color and scent attract insects to the tubes, but the hairs that cloak the inside of the leaves permit the insects to enter but not to get out again. When they fall into the water they drown; a digestive juice dissolves their soft parts, and the plant obtains chemicals it cannot otherwise get from its environment.

Pitcher plants live in peat bogs, where the roots are enmeshed in floating vegetation rather than soil. The water is usually highly acid.

Eight species of pitcher plants occur in North America, most of them in the East, with one species in California.
—G.B.S.

PLACENTA (*See under Mammal*)

PLANKTON

The Plankton Plants and Animals

If one takes a glass of water from a pond and holds it quietly before a sheet of white paper, he will soon notice that there are some tiny specks in the water, scarcely larger than pinpoints, that are actively swimming about. He may also observe that the water has a slight brownish tinge, for he is having a naked-eye view of a vast population of minute plants and animals that inhabit all the waters of the earth. Most are too small for the unaided eye to see, although in the aggregate they often give color to the water. In the glass of water skimmed from the pond are thousands of tiny organisms, a small fraction of the myriads that float and drift about in the waters of every pond, lake, and sea. All the waters of the world are literally teeming with enormous quantities of little organisms in great variety. Collectively they are known as *plankton* and constitute a very basic and important food for many forms of life including mankind.

The word plankton comes from the Greek *planktos* meaning wandering. Al-

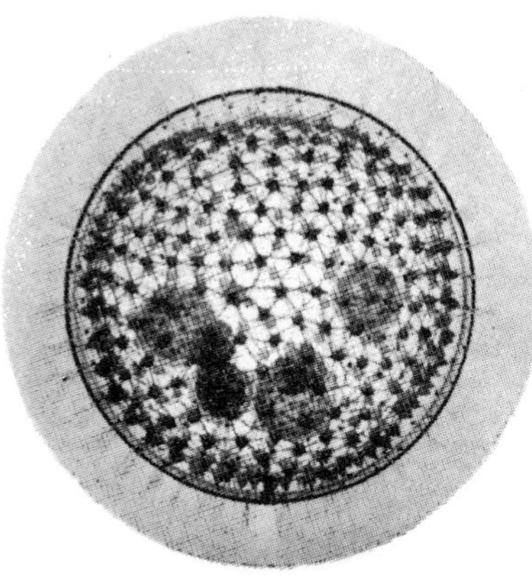

Volvox—a motile colony of one-celled organisms commonly occurring among the plankton species in freshwater ponds and lakes, is often classified as a plant. Because of its motility, however, zoologists classify it in the class Flagellata

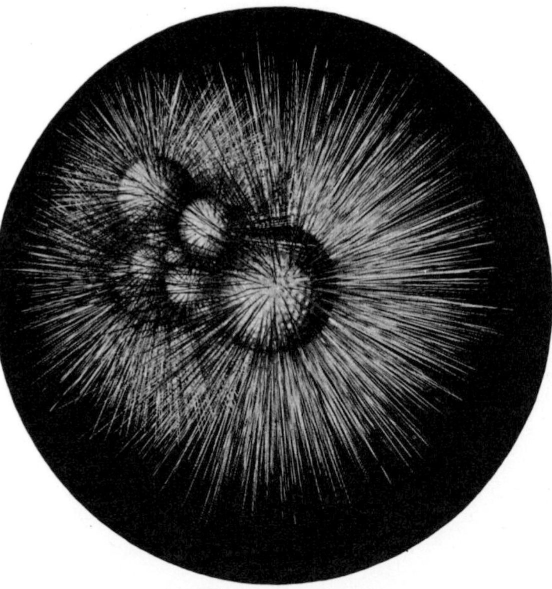

Globigerina, like other members of the order Foramnifera, has a calcareous shell. The shells of this abundant animal fall to the bottom of the ocean where they form "globigerina ooze." It is estimated that some 30 percent of the ocean floor (40,000,000 square miles) is composed of this substance. The living animal is a beautiful luminescent creature that lives near the surface of the sea

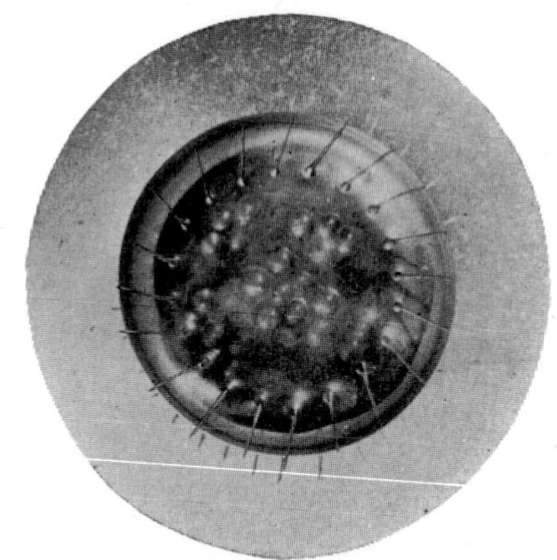

Stephanodiscus

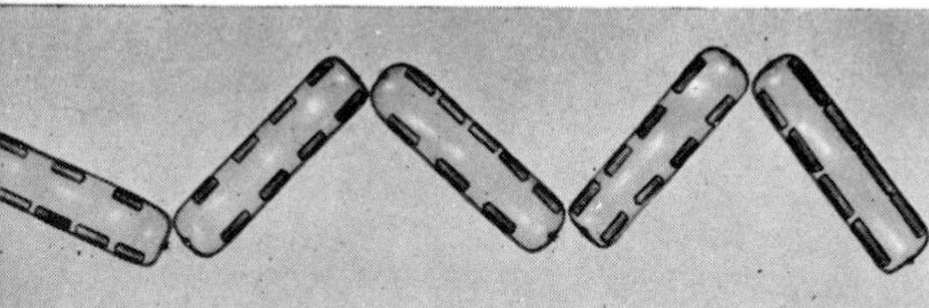

Diatoma

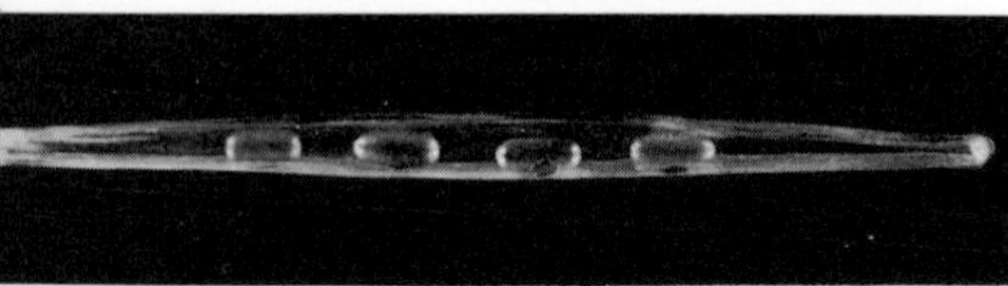

Synedra

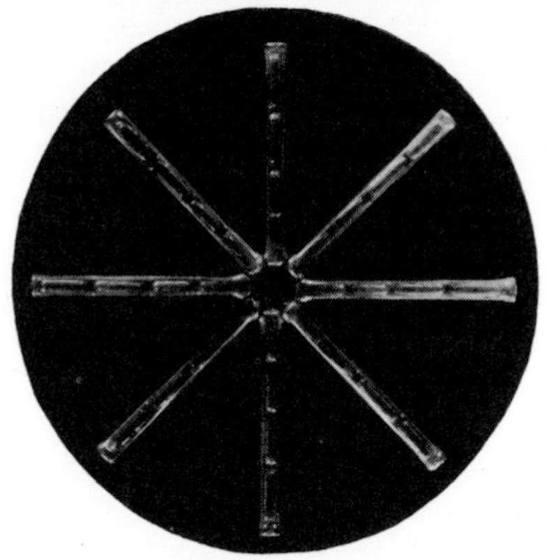

Asterionella

Diatoms are minute chlorophyll-bearing plants encased in a silicious shell consisting of two parts fitted together like a pill box. The species (above) are common freshwater forms

though many plankton organisms are capable of some motion of their own, all are subject to the currents of the water which carry them about. In their helplessness they are in marked contrast to strong swimmers such as fishes, seals, porpoises and whales which, generally speaking, can move about as they please.

For a good look at plankton, a microscope capable of magnifying at least 40 or 50 times is needed. To see some forms, a magnification of 500 times may be required. The creatures to be seen through the microscope, however, will be worth any trouble it may require to find an instrument that will reveal them in their interesting details.

Once one has secured a microscope, he will need a concentration of plankton. To obtain the plankton, use a long (2-3 feet) funnel-shaped collecting bag of fine silk bolting cloth held open by a rim of a stiff wire 8 or 9 inches in diameter. Tow the bag for a half hour or so through a pond, lake, or ocean bay, then turn the bag inside out, immerse the bottom in a small saucer of water and scrape off some of the thin gelatinous coating from the inside of the bag. Place a little of this dense greenish fluid under the microscope and one will be ready to enter into a world of unbelievably fantastic and beautiful Lilliputians of seemingly endless variety.

Here can be seen an independent community of living organisms with its food producing plants, its herbivorous animals that feed on them, its predators that feed on the plant-eaters and one another, its parasites and its scavengers, all contained perhaps within a drop of water (*See Wildlife: The Wildlife Community*).

Plankton Plants

The most numerous plankton organisms are plants. These may comprise considerably more than half, perhaps as much as two-thirds, of the plankton take. Most of them are simple primitive plants consisting of a single cell. They are chiefly algae, and of these, diatoms are the most common groups. Some 1,500 species of diatoms occur in fresh water. In salt water there is an even greater variety. The first plants in the world were similar to these. Today they are still thriving, little changed, and important.

Under the microscope, a diatom is an exquisite thing. It is encased in a transparent "pill box" of glasslike silicon, beautifully etched with lines and pores. Like grasses and leaves, diatoms too contain green chlorophyll and are thus enabled to utilize the sunlight to synthesize carbohydrates from the inorganic substances in the water. In spite of their chlorophyll, however, diatoms look yellow-brown under the microscope. A similar form, the desmids, that occur in fresh water, are a bright green. These and other minute chlorophyll-bearing algae are the basic food-makers of both salt and fresh water. No plankton animals nor plankton-feeders, nor animals that feed on the plankton eaters could exist without them.

To meet this "responsibility" as the basic link in the food chains of all water animals (*see Food Chain*), the diatoms and other plankton plants are capable of rapid multiplication on a vast scale. Individual species recur in rhythmic cycles, at times actually clouding the water with their numbers. Some idea of the enormous quantities of individuals present is gained from accumulations of their cases, which fall to the bottom of the sea when the diatoms die. Some of these great beds of diatom cases, now fossilized and raised above the water, form masses of *diatomacious earth* 40 to 100 or more feet thick and several miles long. The city of Richmond, Virginia is built on such a bed.

Some plankton plants, the freshwater *Volvox*, for example, are both colonial and motile, with many individuals traveling about together in a sphere by means of beating, hairlike cilia. Others, like *Euglena*, have a long, whiplike flagellum and are highly motile. Forms such as these have the green chlorophyll and food-making properties of plants and the motility of animals. They are claimed by botanists as plants and by zoologists as animals (*See Algae*).

Plankton Animals

Plankton animals differ even more than plankton plants in degree of complexity. Nearly every phylum of the animal kingdom is represented in the plankton. There are the one-celled protozoans—the foraminiferans, radiolarians, and dinoflagellates; there are many jellyfishlike medusae, hydroids, and ctenophores; there are tunicates and many others. In addition to these permanent plankton forms, there are the eggs and larvae of fishes, starfishes, sponges, worms, mollusks, and larger crustaceans that "drift" through their infancy as plankton. These temporary plankton animals form quite large seasonal populations; one codfish, for example, lays some 10 million eggs a year, and a single mussel will do the same.

Although most species are microscopic, plankton animals vary in size from the jellyfish, which may be three or four feet across, to one-celled forms so tiny that they filter through the finest silk. These latter are captured by concentrating the contents of considerable volumes of water within the space of a few drops by means of a centrifuge.

Among the most numerous and interesting of the permanent plankton animals are the single-celled protozoans. Some of these, like the Foraminifera, have calcareous shells of great complexity and beauty (*See Foraminifera*). The Radiolaria secrete shells of silica, exquisite in design.

Huge fossil beds of the calcareous remains of the foraminifers have been found. Buildings in Paris, France, are built of stone composed of these; likewise, the pyramids of Egypt. With reference to the stone of which the pyramids are made, Augusta Foote Arnold says in her book, *The Sea Beach at Ebb*

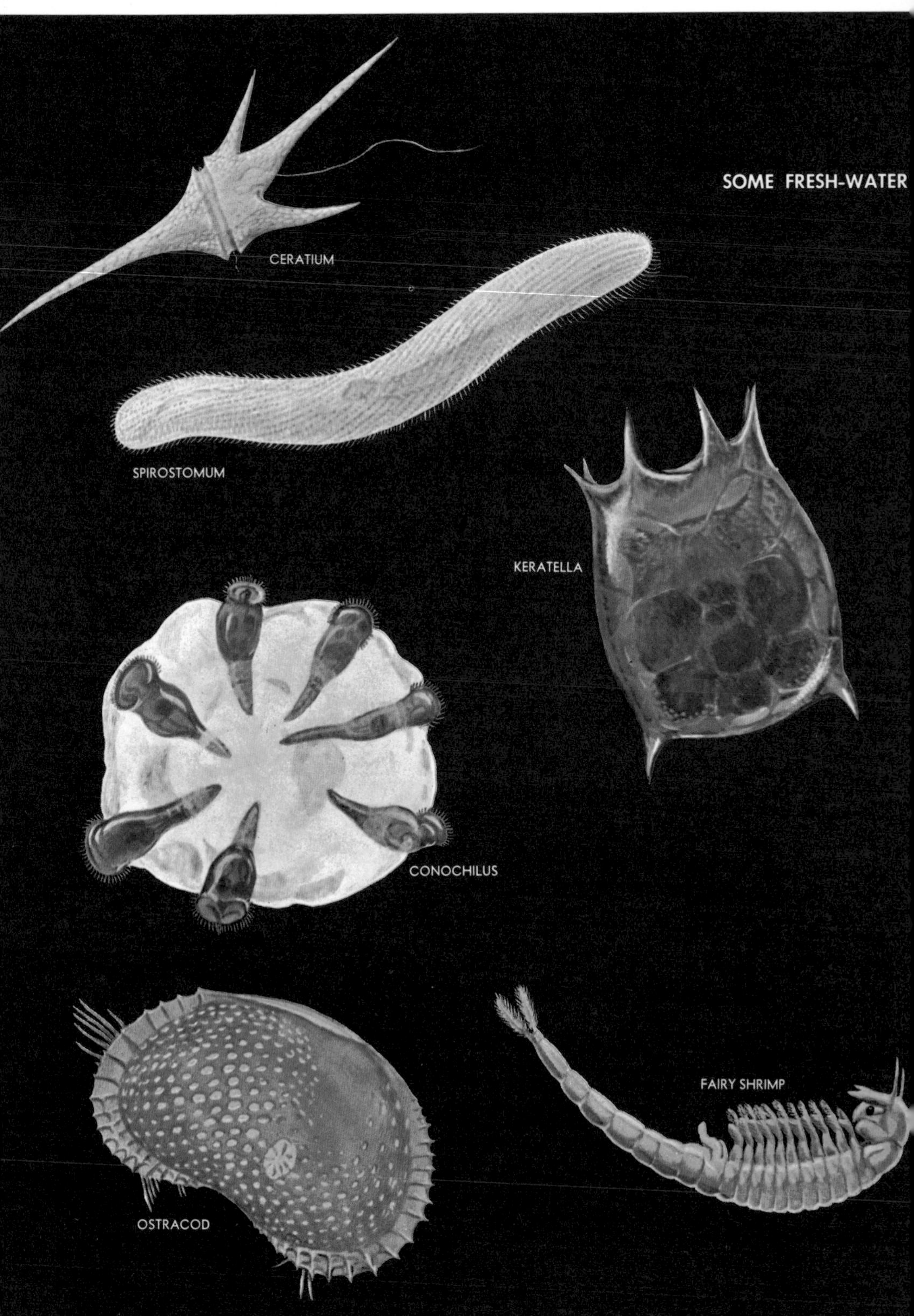
SOME FRESH-WATER
CERATIUM
SPIROSTOMUM
KERATELLA
CONOCHILUS
FAIRY SHRIMP
OSTRACOD

PLANKTON ANIMALS
DAPHNIA
LEPTODORA
CHYDORUS
CYCLOPS
CHAOBORUS
(phantom midge larva)
MYSIS (opossum shrimp)
NAUPLIUS LARVA OF CYCLOPS

Tide, "It is estimated that an ounce of this deposit contains four million of these protozoans!"

Some plankton organisms, particularly marine species, are luminescent when disturbed. The dipping of oars, the wake of a ship, the mere trailing of one's hand in the water at night will set off thousands of tiny "sparks." If one lives or vacations at the seashore, perhaps he can see some at night. Many of these luminescent organisms belong to the group that is not definitely plant and not definitely animal. Noctiluca, one of the Dinoflagellida of the zoologists or one of the Peridiniales of the botanists, is one of the most common luminescent forms. The ctenophores or comb jellies, often called sea walnuts because of their size and shape, leave beautiful trails of light.

The greatest concentration of plankton during the day is some little distance below the surface. In the ocean it is often fifty or more meters down. At night, however, there is usually a vertical migration of the plankton toward the surface. This is accompanied by a similar migration of fishes and other plankton-feeders. Schools of herring may often be seen swimming at the surface at night. Some special food studies of the herring reveal that the stomachs of 240,000 captured daily for a period of three weeks contained an average of 10,000 copepods, a common plankton crustacean. Along with the herring may come seals and small sharks that in turn feed on the plankton animals.

The gills of herring and other plankton-eating fishes are especially adapted for straining out these tiny organisms. The larger toothless whales, the right, finback, and the great sulphur-bottom whales, feed almost entirely on plankton, extracting it by means of their baleen or whalebone.

Light, temperature, specific gravity of the organism, and chemical composition of the water (its salinity, abundance of inorganic substances essential to plantlife, amount of pollution) are the principal factors influencing plankton plantlife. Sensitivity to light governs the vertical distribution of different plankton species and is responsible for shifts in this distribution with daily and seasonal changes in light intensity.

Temperature too plays a part in vertical distribution but its effect is more noticeable in geographic distribution. Each ocean current has its characteristic plankton groupings. In passing from the warm Gulf Stream to the cold Arctic Current off the New England coast, one enters an entirely different plankton community.

Temperature, light, and chemical content of the water, all influence the periodic cycle of plankton abundance. During the cold dark winter months, plankton is relatively scarce, but in March and April diatoms begin to reproduce and there is a sudden outburst of all forms of plankton organisms. Close upon this abundance and adding to it comes the spawning of fishes, worms, mollusks, and other animals whose eggs and larvae form a temporary part of the plankton. This seasonal abundance of plankton is accompanied by an increase in the plankton-feeders and locally by the presence of animals that feed on them: the fish-eating birds such as the cormorants, terns, ospreys; fish-eating mammals such as seals, humpback whales, killer whales; fishermen with their nets and lines.

The *Encyclopedia Britannica* makes the statement, "A spring and summer of organic production in the sea gives origin to about ten tons of moist vegetable substance per acre of sea. This is the marine harvest due to the activity of the vegetable plankton. At present, man reaps only a small fraction of it in the shape of fishes and other edible animals he catches." But if man reaps only a fraction, it may well be that he nevertheless reaps his share. There are many links in the food chain which starts with a diatom and ends with a killer whale, with man or with a cormorant or osprey, and there

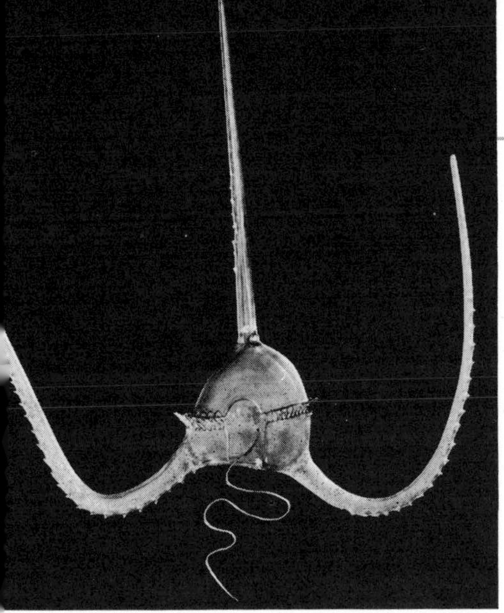

Ceratium is common in stagnant fresh-water pools and reservoirs. It is most abundant in the sea, however, where some species are luminescent. Like many plankton species, Ceratium has the chlorophyll of plants and the motility of animals and cannot be definitely classified as either plant or animal

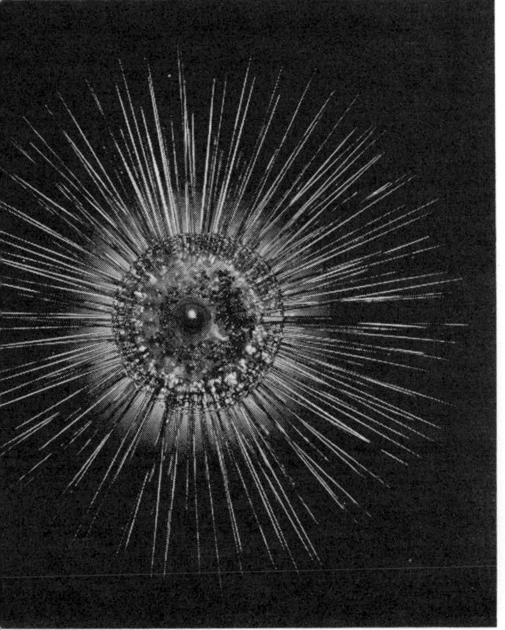

Aulonia hexagonia *is a radiolerian—minute, marine protozoans that occur abundantly near the surface of warm seas. The members of the order Radiolaria secrete shells of silica that are often exquisite in design*

are thousands of different food chains. In Ann Morgan's *Field Book of Ponds and Streams* we read that diatoms form a staple food crop of the water comparable to the grass crop on the land. Diatoms of the sea have been called marine pastures. The dependence of all water creatures upon the minute plankton plants and animals associated with them is absolute. Plankton may be small —microscopic—but it is far from insignificant. It is the staff of life of the water realm. —D.A.T.

Recommended Reading

Algae in Water Supplies—C. M. Palmer. Public Health Service Publication No. 657. Superintendent of Documents, U. S. Printing Office, Washington 25, D. C.

Algae: The Grass of Many Waters—L. H. Tiffany. Charles C. Thomas, Springfield, Illinois.

Animals Without Backbones—Ralph Buchsbaum. University of Chicago Press, Chicago.

Field Book of Ponds and Streams—Ann Haven Morgan. G. P. Putnam's Sons, New York.

Life of Inland Waters—Needham and Lloyd. Comstock Publishing Company, Ithaca, New York.

The Sea Around Us—Rachel Carson, Oxford University Press, New York.

The Seas: Our Knowledge of Life In the Seas and How It Is Gained—F. S. Russell and C. M. Yonge. Frederick Warne and Company, Ltd., New York.

Seashores—A Golden Nature Guide—Herbert S. Zim and Lester Ingle. Simon and Schuster, New York.

PLANT
Plant Kingdom

Plants mostly make their own food, or absorb it, in contrast to animals, which eat their food. All other differences between plants and animals relate to this one.

The plant kingdom may be conveniently subdivided into two subkingdoms, the Thallophyta, which include the bacteria, algae, and fungi, and the Embryophyta, which include the mosses, liverworts, ferns and fernlike plants, and seed plants. All the familiar green land plants large enough to be individually visible to the naked eye are embryophytes.

The thallophytes are an extremely diverse group. The name reflects the fact that the plant body is a thallus; i.e. it is not divided into roots, stems, and leaves. A frequently used classification recognizes eight divisions of thallophytes, the Schizophyta, Rhodophyta, Chlorophyta, Euglenophyta, Pyrrophyta, Chrysophyta, Phaeophyta, and Fungi.

The Schizophyta are the most primitive division. They differ from all other organisms in the relatively simple (prokaryotic) organization of their protoplasm, which lacks the complex nucleus and cytoplasmic organelles of other (eukaryotic) organisms. The Schizophyta consist of two classes, the Schizomycetes (bacteria) and the Cyanophyceae (blue-green algae). Bacteria are microscopic and are best known as agents of disease and decay, but they play an important role in the balance of nature and are particularly important in the nitrogen cycle. Some bacteria carry on a primitive type of photosynthesis in which oxygen is not released. Some others, such as the iron bacteria, make their food chemosynthetically, using energy that is released in certain inorganic chemical changes (*See under Bacteria*).

All the plants that carry on typical (oxygen-releasing) photosynthesis, but that do not have the structural peculiarities of embryophytes, are known as algae. This takes in all the thallophytes except the bacteria and fungi. Most algae are aquatic, but some of the smaller ones are terrestrial, usually in moist places (*See Algae*).

The blue-green algae and the red algae (Rhodophyta) have phycobilin pigments in addition to chlorophyll, and they lack motile cells of any kind. Some phycobilins are blue (phycocyanins); others are red (phycoerythrins). Phycocyanins usually predominate in the blue-green algae, but some have more phycoerythrin, and the Red Sea probably got its name from the abundance of *Trichodesmium*, a blue-green algae that is red. Some blue-green algae live in very hot water; they are largely responsible for the brilliant colors around hot springs in Yellowstone Park. All blue-green algae are small, and many are microscopic unicells.

The red algae are nearly all multicellular and readily visible, forming well developed, often compactly branched thalli. Most of them are marine, occurring in the intertidal zone or submerged in coastal waters in tropical and warm-temperate regions. Some of them become heavily calcified through chemical activities related to photosynthesis; these coralline algae contribute to the growth of coral reefs.

The green algae (Chlorophyta) are chemically much like the embryophytes, to which they are usually considered ancestral. Some are microscopic unicells, but others are more complex. The stringy green coating often seen on rocks in streams usually consists largely of green algae, as does the greenish crust (like a faint wash of paint) often seen on tree trunks. The red snow sometimes found at high altitudes is reddened by certain green algae that have an additional red pigment, but most green algae are truly green. *Ulva*, the sea lettuce, looks superficially much like a lettuce leaf.

The euglenoids (Euglenophyta) are a small group consisting largely of unicellular flagellates with certain structural and chemical peculiarities. They are poised on the boundary between the plant and animal kingdoms; some are foodmakers, and others are food-eaters.

The Chrysophyta and Pyrrophyta are microscopic, often unicellular algae that have a high proportion of yellow or brownish carotenoids in relation to the amount of chlorophyll (the essential photosynthetic green pigment). The most familiar chrysophytes are the diatoms (class Bacillariophyceae), with a highly silicified, two-piece cell wall, and without flagella during the vegetative stage. They make up a large part of the vegetable plankton of the cooler parts of the ocean, and they are also common in fresh water. Like other chrysophytes, diatoms store food as oils instead of starch. The Pyrrophyta make starch and and have a cellulosic (or no) cell wall; most of them are unicellular flagellates. The dinoflagellates (class Dinophyceae) are the most familiar pyrrophytes. They are mostly marine, and in warm regions they may become so abundant as to cause "red tides."

The brown algae (Phaeophyta) contain a brown carotenoid, fucoxanthin, as an accessory photosynthetic pigment. They are multicellular and often become very large. They are especially common along the seashore in the cooler parts of the world, but some of them float in the open ocean, notably in the Sargasso Sea. The most familiar brown algae are the kelps (*See under Kelp*).

The molds, mildews, mushrooms, yeasts, and similar plants that do not carry on photosynthesis constitute the fungi. Some are parasites (chiefly of other plants), but others cause fermentation or decay. The slime molds (class Myxomycetes) are an anomalous group that engulf small bits of food in an amoeboid manner. The other three classes of fungi (Phycomycetes, Ascomycetes, and Basidiomycetes) are distinguished by microscopic structure features (*See under Fungus*). Some of them, especially the Basidiomycetes, live in partnership with plant roots, forming mycorhizae. Others, especially Ascomycetes, entrap and protect certain algae (chiefly green algae), forming lichens (*See Lichen*).

The embryophytes are a relatively homogeneous subkingdom with many structural and chemical features in common. The name comes from the fact that the fertilized egg begins its growth as a parasite on the parent plant, forming an embryo. A frequently used classification recognizes eight divisions, the Bryophyta, Psilophyta, Lepidophyta, Calamophyta, Filicophyta, Coniferophyta, Cycadophyta, and Anthophyta. The last seven of these characteristically have specialized conducting tissues (xylem and phloem) and are often grouped into a single division Tracheophyta, the vascular plants.

In bryophytes the sporophyte generation is scarcely more than a stage in the reproduction of the green, photosynthetic gametophyte, to which it is attached. Lacking xylem and phloem, the bryophytes are always small, not more than a few inches high. There are three classes, the Musci, or mosses; Hepaticae, or liverworts; and Anthocerotae, or horned liverworts (*See Mosses and Liverworts*).

In the Psilophyta, Lepidophyta, Calamophyta, and Filicophyta the gametophyte and sporophyte generations are detached and physiologically independent of each other at maturity. Only the sporophyte has vascular tissues and reaches any considerable size. These several groups are sometimes taken as a single division Pteridophyta. The psilophytes, relatively simple in structure, with green stems and without leaves, have only three modern species, but are well known as fossils and may be ancestral to all other vascular plants. The whisk-fern, *Psilotum nudum*, is the most familiar psilophyte. The Lepidophyta (club mosses) are an ancient group with small, alternate leaves and axillary sporangia. Common and diverse in the Paleozoic Era, they are represented today by a dwindling remnant, *Lycopodium* and *Selaginella* being the most familiar genera (*See under Club Mosses and Horsetails*). The calamophyta, with whorled, mostly small leaves, and terminal cones, are another dwindling group. Only the genus *Equisetum* (horsetails and scouring rushes) survives today. The Filicophyta, or ferns, are the most familiar modern pteridophytes (*See under Fern*). They commonly have large, compound leaves on which the sporangia are borne.

In the Coniferophyta, Cycadophyta, and Anthophyta the gametophyte generation is reduced to a stage in the re production of the sporophyte. These are

Fucus, a brown alga, is a multicellular plant that is common in shallow coastal waters. Its branching thallus is bouyed up by many gas-containing vesicles

The deadly amanita mushroom is a common fungus that derives its nourishment from dead and decaying matter. At its base is a cup from which the stalk arises

The plant kingdom is divided into two subkingdoms. The subkingdon Thallophyta—a heterogeneous group of plants that lack division into roots, stems, and leaves—includes the bacteria, the algae, and the fungi. The bacteria are all microscopic plants that are well known as agents of disease but are also important in the processes of decay and, in some cases, nitrogen fixing. These minute plants do not release oxygen in the photosynthetic process, and some produce their food chemosynthetically. All of the algae produce oxygen as a bi-product of their photo synthetic processes, while the fungi do not carry on photosynthesis at all but gain their nourishment from other plants, either parasitically, symbiotically, by engulfing bits of organic matter, or by fermentation and decay

Club mosses, a flourishing group of plants 400 million years ago, are represented by only a few genera today. They have small, alternate leaves.

Ferns, sometimes grouped with club mosses and other plants in the division Pteridophyta, usually have large, compound leaves

Conifers, such as this sugar pine, have seeds that are exposed at the time of polination. The conifers and cycads are called gymnosperms

The flowering plants, such as this magnolia, are the dominant group of plants today and are represented by some 200,000 species

The subkingdom Embryophyta, is a relatively homogeneous group of plants that have many structural and chemical features in common. The embryophytes all begin growth as a fertilized egg that is parasitic on the parent plant and forms an embryo. Eight divisions of this subkingdom are usually recognized. The bryophytes (mosses, liverworts, and horned liverworts) lack vascular structures and are never more than a few inches high. The remaining seven divisions, Psilophyta (psilophytes); Lepidophyta (club mosses), Calamophyta (calamophytes); Filicophyta (ferns); Coniferophyta (conifers); Cycadophyta (cycads); and Anthophyta (flowering plants) are often grouped in a single division Tracheophyta—plants having vascular structures. The flowering plants are divided into two classes: the monocots (having a single embryo leaf in the seed) and the dicots (having two embryo leaves in the seed) the seed plants, sometimes taken as a single division Spermatophyta (*See under Dicotyledon*). In the conifers and cycads the ovules (young seeds) are exposed at the time of pollination, and the pollen grain lands on the ovule; such plants are called gymnosperms, from the naked seeds, which are commonly borne in cones. The body of the female gametophyte commonly serves as a food storage tissue in gymnosperm seeds. The most familiar conifers are trees such as spruces, firs, pines, and cedars, with small, often needlelike leaves and excurrently branched trunks (*See Evergreen*). The cycads, although well known as fossils, are represented today by less than a hundred species, these with large, pinnately compound leaves and short, mostly unbranched trunks.

The Anthophyta, or flowering plants, have about 200,000 species and make up the dominant vegetation of the earth. They have the ovules enclosed in an ovary, whence they are often called angiosperms. The female gametophyte is represented only by a minute embryo sac in the developing ovule, and the seed has a unique food-storage tissue, the endosperm. The Anthophyta may be divided into two classes, the Monocotyledonae and Dicotyledonae. Monocots mostly have one cotyledon (embryo leaf in the seed) and typically have parallel-veined leaves. They usually have scattered vascular bundles in the stem, and they lack typical secondary (thickening growth. The flower parts are most often in sets of three, seldom four, never five. Lilies, grasses, rushes, orchids, irises, palms, and aroids are familiar monocots. Dicots ordinarily have two cotyledons and net-veined leaves. They usually have the vascular bundles in a ring, and they typically show secondary growth, often becoming trees. The flower parts are often in sets of five, less often four or three. Oaks, maples, cherries, roses, violets, carrots, potatoes, sunflowers, and ragweeds are among the many familiar dicots. —A.C.

Recommended Reading

Introductory Botany—Arthur Cronquist. Harper & Row, New York.
The Plant Kingdom—Harold Bold. Prentice-Hall, Englewood Cliffs, New Jersey.
The Plants—Frits W. Went. Time, Inc., New York.

Some Facts about Wild Plants In and Out of Doors

Dandelions on the Lawn

Children gathering dandelion blossome on the lawn are gathering gold. The more children know about dandelions the more certain they will be that they *are* gathering gold. It is the kind of wealth that pays dividends throughout life.

Gather a bouquet of dandelions to show the unfurling of the flower from the earliest bud to the mature seed. Eight or ten specimens will show the complete life history. Arrange them from youngest to oldest. You really have a motion picture show before you—but—having the dandelions in your hand is no proof that you see the story.

Break apart a dandelion blossom and remove the smallest yellow strap. That is one flower. Now you know whether dandelion blossoms are a flower or a bouquet. Next you might test your eyesight. How many teeth are there on the end of the strap? That number indicates the number of petals that the ancestral dandelion had. The two "horns" at the top of the flower are stigmas which catch the pollen brought from other dandelions by insects. If you have a hand lens you can count the stamens that make up the "collar" just below the stigmas. There are 10. Touch the stamens with your fingers and learn where the insects get their pollen. Look along your dandelion "picture film" and decide what the white thing at the bottom of each flower is going to become.

There will be as many dandelion seeds as there are flowers. They sit on the *torus*, or receptacle. There are as many dimples in the torus seat as there were seeds. Take the oldest seed you can find. Let it float in the air. Which part of the parachute hits the ground first? Nature knows how to plant seeds. Examine another seed. Which end has teeth? Test your eyesight again. Which way do the teeth point? Perhaps the teeth help anchor the seed.

The green things on the outside of the blossom are called *bracts*. The dandelion has an interesting way of folding up the flowers and seeds when it rains. Sometimes the bracts close over the flowers and seeds at night. When the seeds have at last ripened they spread out their white silky tufts in a perfect sphere for the winds to catch—and off they go to start new dandelions.

Dig up a dandelion plant and see the fleshy root. The root, when made into dandelion "coffee" produces a bitter fluid that most children dislike but you will enjoy making rubber. Place some of the milk from the root on your thumb. The milk is called lactic acid and is like the lactic secretion from the rubber tree. Now rub the sticky lactic acid with your forefinger and you will soon have some black rubber that is elastic. You can read in a book that it is possible to make rubber from milk, but "seeing is believing," and one will remember it longer.

Next get two dandelion leaves. One leaf should have as few teeth as possible and the next one as many large teeth as possible. This difference is called *variation* and what a big variation there is. The French must have noticed the teeth too. They called the plant *dandelion.* The word really means *dent de lion*, or the *teeth of the lion.*

"Evergreens" for the Winter Window Shelf

Emerson says, "Nature reflects the

On one dandelion plant one may see all of the stages in the development of the seeds from buds and flowers to the tiny seeds that are carried away on little parachutes by the wind

color of the spirit." If you give yourself over to the spirit of finding gold, you will find it at any time of the year. Try it in late fall. Get as many congenial companions as you can find. Carry a shovel, and flowerpots, with the idea of getting "evergreens" for the window shelf. Your pot of gold will be winter rosettes in the form of yarrow, mullein, Queen Anne's lace, and field daisies. Whoever pots the yarrow will have something as beautiful as a fern. In London the mullein is called American velvet plant. Queen Anne's lace—there is a plant you will appreciate, and you don't have to wait for "Queen Anne" to weave its white flower lace; its feathery leaves are exquisite things themselves. The field daisies will reward you by presenting gold in a white setting in midwinter. Dandelions in a flowerpot will blossom in a few weeks. If you have been successful in discovering these winter rosettes you can get added pleasure by discovering other rosettes. There is oxalis that resembles shamrock, or St. Johnswort with its "pinhole" leaves. Pot a pennyroyal so as to have a whiff of mint in the winter. Try a nibble next February and see if that isn't surprising.

A Winter Bouquet

Training the eye always brings new gold. Winter bouquets are harmonies of form as well as color. You may have fun arranging cattails with different lengthed stems in a very large holder. Collect dried stalks of milkweed, mullein, and other dried plants and try grouping some of these in a vase. Some people may want to put paint or tinsel on winter bouquests, but it seems doubtful if they have stopped to see what a good job nature herself did in form and color. It is hard to improve on nature. When tramping the fields in winter, you may meet some birds that also are out "weeding." They like the weeds because they contain seeds that make an ideal breakfast. Spread some of this feast on your feeding tray and coax these birds to call on you.

The Plant Geography Game

Plan a hike for your group that will take you through a field into the woods. As you go along, try playing the *plant geography game.* It is played this way. There are many common plants of our fields and roadsides that were introduced from Europe. John Smith could not have picked them for Pocahontas because they weren't here to pick. There are other

The thistle plant remains green throughout the winter and is often kept on window shelves

plants that were well known to the Indians. These are native, or American plants. You, as leader, say the name of any of these plants and when you give the signal members of your group say "European" or "American"—according to whether they believe that the plants were introduced or are native. It won't be long before everyone will be giving the correct answer. The funny thing is that no one will know *how* he knows. Of course the first plants you name should be fairly obvious: dandelion (European), Indian turnip (American). If you name a plant they do not know, it is omitted. Have someone try you on these wild flowers: 1, English plantain; 2, joe-pye weed; 3, arbutus; 4, ragweed; 5, burdock; 6, mocassin flower; 7, white daisy; 8, pepper grass; 9, cardinal flower; 10, columbine; 11, pipsissewa; 12, pitcher plant; 13, anemone. *(See answers on next page.)*

Could you finally guess whether they were native or introduced? How did you know? Before you read any further try to find the "secret" by which you "guessed" correctly whether they were American or European.

The surprising thing is that most of the weed rosettes that you potted for "winter evergreens" are European. That is also true of the winter bouquet. The wild flowers that are being exterminated, on the other hand are "vanishing Americans." Perhaps you would like to try again to solve the problem.

Now try reasoning again. Tell as many things as you can that are common to the European plants that have been introduced. Tell as many things as you can that are common to the native American plants. Maybe you would be willing to write two columns of differences before reading any more. Now score your paper. If there are several of you it will be fun to see who has the highest score.

In general, plants with long periods of flowering that produce many seeds and are tolerant of many kinds of soil and growing places may be freely picked. These include members of the composite family, many of them so common we call them weeds. The plants that are delicate, produce few seeds, and require a rather special set of growing conditions, should not be picked. These include many spring wild flowers, orchids, certain of the lilies, and others. Those that may be picked in moderation occupy a sort of middle of the road position. The best way to determine these is to make a survey of the plants in your area.

Answers to Quiz in Plant Geography Game

(1) E; (2) A; (3) A; (4) E; (5) E; (6) A; (7) E;
(8) E; (9) A; (10) A; (11) A; (12) A; (13) A.

DIFFERENCES BETWEEN EUROPEAN AND NATIVE AMERICAN WILD FLOWERS

Item	*Native Wild Flowers*	*Introduced European*
1. Where grow?	Forests	Open fields, gardens roadsides
2. Amount of sun?	Shade loving	Sun enduring
3. Texture of plant?	Tender	Tough vagrants
4. Seeds?	Comparatively few	Many
5. Distribution?	Not so easily distributed	Easily distributed
6. Number of plants?	Being exterminated by clearing of land	Can survive
7. Hairs?	Tend to be smooth	Tend to be hairy to conserve moisture
8. Soils?	Dark, rich humus	Anywhere, even gravel
9. When flower?	Early spring before leaves of trees come forth	All summer
10. Family?	Orchids, heaths and others	Many composites

Daisy

Goldcrest and bladderwort

Dandelion

Black-eyed Susan

Things to Know and Do

The official flower for the Province of Ontario, Canada, is *Trillium grandiflorum.* Does your state have an official flower? Where in *your* town are these acres in which the land, the flowers, the trees, the water, and the hills are the possession of all? (*See Nature Center.*) Make an inventory of *your* forest preserves and parks. What rare wild flowers grow in each area as harbingers of spring? Who takes care of this wealth? How many acres are there? How much did it cost? What is its value? Is there any "roadside wealth" in your town? Where? Some folks do not really understand how this nature wealth belongs to all the people. How do "thoughtless" people destroy the wealth of wild flowers that belong to all the citizens? What has your town done to encourage picnickers to be thoughtful and to leave the wild flowers for others to enjoy? Some New England states have a law against collecting the rare climbing fern, *Lygodium palmatum.* Are there any wild flowers in your state that are protected by law? On many highways in New York and other states it is against the law to break branches off the azaleas and flowering dogwood that grow along the roadway. In fact, autoists are not allowed to take any of the shrubbery and wild flowers. Why was it necessary to pass such a law?

A nature trail with individual plant labels is instructive. Green enamel is brushed on a wooden or metal plaque and the information is lettered on this background (*See Nature Trail*). People become interested and vandalism negligible. If your town does not put up posters in the park to help save the wild flowers you might like to try your skill in making signs that are appropriate and artistic. Rustic signs are the most pleasing. Burning letters in slabs of wood is a method that fits into the surroundings. There may be a bog in your town that has a wide range of interesting plants (*See Bog*). Perhaps it is about to be destroyed and needs some one to champion it for a wildflower preserve. There are many organizations that will be glad to help you—The Society for the Preservation of Native New England Plants, Horticultural Hall, Boston, Mass., The Wild Flower Preservation Society, 3740 Oliver Street, N.W., Washington, D.C., your state Agricultural College Extension Service, your state Conservation Department, your local nature and conservation societies (*See also under Wild flower*).

—W.G.V.

Recommended Reading

The Amateur Naturalist's Handbook—Vinson Brown. Little, Brown & Co., Boston.

Beginner's Guide to Wild Flowers—Ethel Hinckley Hausman. G.P. Putnam's Sons, Inc., New York.

The Book of Nature Hobbies—Ted Pettit. Didier Publishers, New York.

Exploring Nature with Your Child—Dorothy Edwards Shuttlesworth. Greystone Press, New York.

Field Book of American Wild Flowers—Schuyler Matthews. G.P. Putnam's Sons, New York.

Field Book of Nature Activities—William Hillcourt. G.P. Putnam's Sons, New York.

Field Book of Western Wild Flowers—Margaret Armstrong. G.P. Putnam's Sons, New York.

Helpful Audubon Nature Bulletins: How to Build a Nature Trail, Ferns, Parade of Spring Wild Flowers, Wildlife Preserves. National Audubon Society, New York.

Nature Recreation—William Gould Vinal. American Humane Education Society, Boston.

Plants of Woodland and Wayside—SuZan N. Swain. Garden City Books, Garden City, New York.

Sharp Eyes: A Rambler's Calendar of 52 Weeks

Indoor Plants—Selection and Care

Many interesting plants can be grown in the home or schoolroom, and many interesting facts discovered about them through simple experiments easily worked out on a windowsill.

Plants are magicians with the power to turn an unattractive den or classroom into a beautiful and pleasant place for work. No room is really too dark to support a border of living green. Plants are assets in other ways too. They are good visual aids capable of enhancing

English, geography, history, social studies, and science. Many plants have fascinating stories closely interwoven with folklore. Because plants are living things needing light, air, food, water, and rest in order to thrive and grow, learning to care for them teaches valuable lessons about how to care for ourselves and provides an activity to be shared and enjoyed by all.

To make an indoor garden a success one will need to consider carefully the following points:

Light. Plants vary greatly in their light requirements. It is important to select plants that grow well under the light conditions available in one's room, and in the particular part of the room where it is planned to place them. The following lists give an interesting choice.

Windows with good light (south, southeast, southwest exposures)
Begonia semperflorens – Flowering begonia
Beloperone guttata – shrimp plant
Chrysanthemum frutescens – marguerites
Coleus (varieties) – coleus
Desert plants – (see section on Sand Gardens)
Flowering bulbs – narcissus (all types); tulips; hyacinths; crocus; amaryllis; calla lily.
Impatiens (varieties) – snapweeds, touch-me-nots
Kalanchoe tomentosa, tubiflora, daigremontiana – kalanchoe
Morea – butterfly iris, wedding flower
Pelargonium (varieties) – geranium
Saintpaulia ionantha – African violet (east or west preferable; southern exposure provided they are protected from hot sun)

Windows with good light (north exposure)
Asparagus plumosus – fern asparagus
Asparagus sprengeri – fern asparagus
Aspidistra elatior – common aspidistra
Begonia (foliage varieties)
Chlorophytum – spider plant
Cissus rhombifolia – grape ivy
Coleus (varieties) – coleus
Cyperus alternifolius – umbrella sedge (keep pot in saucer of water)
Dieffenbachia – dumb cane
Dracaena (varieties) – dragon plant
Ferns – Boston, holly, pteris, bird's nest
Ficus elastica – India rubber tree
Grevillea robusta – silk oak
Ivy (varieties)
Pandanus utilis – screw pine
Pelargonium – geranium (ivy and scented-leaved varieties)
Peperomia (varieties)
Philodendron(varieties)
Scindapsus aureus – ivy arum
Rhoeo discolor – oyster plant
Sansevieria trifasciata variety *laurentii* – snakeplant, or bowstring hemp

Grape ivy

Asparagus fern

Umbrella plant

Saxifraga sarmentosa—strawberry "geranium"
Tolmiea menziesii—Pick-a-back plant

Windows with poor light (opening off courtyard)
Aglaonema modestum—Chinese evergreen
Asparagus sprengeri—fern asparagus
Aspidistra elatior—common aspidistra
Crassula arborescens—jade plant
Ficus elastica—India rubber tree
Ivy (varieties)
Pandanus utilis—common screwpine
Philodendron (varieties)
Sansevieria var. *laurentii*—snakeplant, or bowstring hemp
Tradescantia flaminensis—wandering Jew
Zebrina pendula—purple-leaved wandering Jew

Temperature. A good average room temperature for plant growth is from 65° to 70° F. with perhaps a drop of as much as 10° at night. Most plants do better in cold rooms than in hot. Avoid "cooking" and drying plants by placing them directly over hot radiators. Avoid chilling and freezing them by leaving them close to windows on cold days and nights. Unless the day is excessively cold, a thick layer of newspaper between the plants and the window will be sufficient protection for winter nights. It will be wise to place plants at some distance from windows over winter weekends.

After weeks of acquaintance, plants often seem like pets. Children will welcome the idea of taking them home and caring for them over the long holidays (Thanksgiving, Christmas, and Easter). To protect from cold on these journeys to and from school, wrap the plants well in a thick jacket of newspaper. Plants, like people, need good fresh air but will suffer from drafts. If necessary to open a window, first move the plants to a protected place, or open a window that will not let cold air blow directly on the plants.

Water. Water plants only when they need it, that is, when the soil feels dry. More plants suffer from too much water than from too little. When watering plants do it thoroughly so that the soil is wet to the bottom of the pot. Then wait until the soil is dry before watering again. Plants that grow fast can stand more watering than slow growers. If the leaves become covered with dust and soot sprinkle well to wash them clean. A once-a-week shower bath is a very good plan. When plants are growing strongly put rations of plant food in their water. Outdoors, old leaves and plants add minerals and humus to the soil; indoors, these must be supplied by commercial brands of plant food, such as Vigoro, Hyponex, Plantabbs, Rapid-Gro, Stimuplant and others. *Be careful not to overfeed,* and never feed a sick plant. Most plants take some rest in the winter. It is best to wait until early spring to feed.

Soil. A good average soil for flowerpots consists of two parts garden soil, one part leaf mold (layer of topsoil about two inches deep found beneath trees) and one part sharp sand (builder's sand). To each peck of soil add five tablespoons of bone meal. Before placing the soil in pots, insure good drainage by placing a layer of pebbles or broken bits of flower pots on the bottom. Common, red, unglazed flowerpots are considered best. These are porous and permit transfer of air and moisture. Plants will grow better in these than in the glazed or painted pots. Unglazed pots may be fitted loosely inside glazed pottery, however, without harm to the plants. About once a week, and only when the soil is dry, scratch the surface soil to a depth of about half an inch with an old kitchen fork. This will help keep the soil fresh and the plants will breathe better.

Insects. Insects most frequently found on house plants are: small greenlice (*see Aphid*) seen on the growing tips of the plants; mealy bugs on the under surface of the leaves or in the niches between the stems; and scale insects, which are insects with a hardened outer surface.

Control of ordinary lice. Spray affected parts of the plant with the following solution: one-half ounce of white mild soap, dissolved in two quarts of water, to which add one-half teaspoonful of nicotine sulphate (obtainable at a seed store).

Control of mealy bugs. Wipe affected parts of plant with cheesecloth moistened in the above solution, thoroughly freeing the plant of the insects. Or keep a little bottle of alcohol and a fine paintbrush handy. Touch the insect with alcohol but do not touch the plant.

Control of scale insects. Spraying does absolutely no good. Each scale must be raised from the plant with a toothpick or a dull pointed knife, and the insect beneath killed. Then wash the plant leaves with the soap solution, using a soft brush.

Sand gardens. Many interesting plants do well in sandy soil. The soil should not be pure sand, however, but a mixture of one-half garden soil and one-half sand. To give your sand garden a pleasing and more natural appearance, top this soil mixture with a one-half inch layer of pure sand. Try growing some of the following: *Kalanchoe pinnata;* christmas cactus; crassula; houseleek, or hen and chickens; *Kleinia*—African succulent; sedums; *Mesembryanthemum*—fig marigold; *Euphorbia* — poinsettia, crown-of-thorns. All are sun-loving plants of desert and dune and require direct sunlight.

Window boxes. Select plants for window boxes according to their light requirements. Arrange the taller plants at the back and place trailing plants in front to overhang. Excessively tall plants, such as the rubber plant, really have no place in a window box. No one plant should be so large as to dominate the rest. Good trailers for the front of your box are: *Tradescantia*—wandering Jew; trailing or drooping coleus; English ivy; ivy-leaved geranium; *Saxifrage sarmentosa; Ficus pumila*—climbing fig; *Zebrina pendula*—purple-leaved wandering Jew. Trailing plants are attractive in hanging baskets and wall brackets. Suspend a basket from a swinging bracket attached to the window frame.

Windowsill Activities with Plants

It is fun to experiment, and facts discovered in this way, at first hand, will be long remembered. It is full of surprise and adventure too, for the exact outcome is unknown. Here are a few simple experments designed to give children a better understanding of the care of plants through enabling them to see for themselves.

A. Experiments with light and water.

1. Effect of light. Assemble three groups of plants, similar in size, each containing a geranium, English ivy, wandering Jew, fern, and a seedling plant of some garden annual such as batchelor's button, marigold, aster, or zinnia. Place one group where the plants will receive direct sunlight, the second in partial sunlight or in a north window, the third where it will receive poor light. Care for each group carefully for one month and see what happens. Keep a record week by week.

2. Effect of water. Using one group of plants, try the following: Give too much water (water thoroughly once a day), then give too little water (that is do not water thoroughly, just wet the top of the soil), later give no water at all for a period of three days. Report what happens.

3. Effect of bathing. Give some of your plants a good shower bath once a week and gently wash the under surfaces of the leaves of some of the broad-leaved hardier plants. Refrain from washing others of the same variety and observe result.

B. Making plant cuttings (slipping)

It is interesting to know how to make cuttings for it will enable one to grow an entirely new plant from a small branch of an old one. Follow these directions carefully:

1. Prepare a rooting pan for cuttings—a shallow tray about three or four inches deep filled with sharp builder's sand that has been sterilized with boiling water. Have sand moist and warm.

2. Select firm little plant branches about four inches long (they should not be old and tough). With a sharp knife cut diagonally downward just below a node or leaf stem joint. Remove all leaves excepting two or three at the end. With a finger or a pencil make a straight hole in the sand and insert the cutting sticking it as far down as the lowest set of leaves. Press sand firmly about the cuttings. Cover over with newspaper for a few days, then place in sunny window. Keep plants in moist sand until they have taken root. That will take almost three weeks, although keeping them over a warm radiator during this time will speed the rooting. But care should be taken not to let them become too hot.

After the roots have formed, lift the cuttings from the sand gently by slipping a cake spatula down under the plants (pulling them out will injure the new roots), and plant immediately. To plant, first place a little soil in the bottom of the pot; support the plant so that it rests on the earth, and add more soil until the pot is nearly filled. Press down firmly. The soil should come to about one-half inch from the top of the pot.

Common aspidistra

3. Try rooting cuttings in a Forsythe pan. This pan is almost self-watering and can easily be constructed in the following manner. Take a large baking dish about three or four inches deep, and in the center place a small unglazed flowerpot with drain hole tightly corked. Fill the baking dish with moist sand and the flowerpot with water. The water will seep slowly through the porous sides of the flowerpot, although not in quite sufficient amount to keep the sand moist enough. You will need to water the sand occasionally when necessary. Of course you will have to keep water in the pot.

C. Growing plants from seeds

1. Have a citrous garden. Save the seeds from oranges, lemons, and grapefruit. Let them dry and ripen, then plant them in flower pots. Find out what the word, citrous, means. Plant date seeds in fern or ivy pots until they start to grow. (It may take them three months to start.)

2. It is lots of fun to raise the following plants from seeds. These are some many boys and girls rarely use. Try them. *Asparagus sprengeri,* fern asparagus; *Mimosa pudica,* sensitive plant; *Pelargonium zonale,* zonale geranium.

D. Playing plant detective

1. Have a good time discovering where

all these plants come from and how they arrived in America.

2. Find out about other members of the families that these house plants belong to. Some are famous for the help they have been to people in saving lives, curing illnesses, and providing useful substances. —E.E.S. and M.D.

Recommended Reading

The Adventure Book of Growing Plants—Frances M. Miner. Capitol Publishing Company, Inc., New York.

All About House Plants: The Amateur's Guide to the Successful Indoor Culture of Flowers, Foliage Plants, Shrubs, Bulbs and Vines—Montague Free. The American Garden Guild, Inc. & Doubleday and Co., Inc., New York.

Bulbs — Brooklyn Botanic Garden, Brooklyn, New York.

Gardening: A New World for Children—Sally Wright. The Macmillan Company, New York.

House Plants—Brooklyn Botanic Garden, Brooklyn, New York.

How to Grow House Plants—Millicent Selsam. Morrow Junior Books, New York.

Poison Ivy and Other Poisonous Plants

In spite of the oft-repeated warning, "Leaflets three, let it be; berries white, hide from sight," thousands of people each summer suffer an itching torment from the effects of poison ivy. Some are confined to bed, others hospitalized, simply because they never bothered to learn to recognize this irritating plant. Certainly no teacher or youth leader responsible for children out of doors should neglect to make clear the hazard of exposure to this plant and how to recognize poison ivy and thus to avoid it.

Experts agree that one's sensitivity is created by repeated contacts with poison ivy, and that no one can assume that he is permanently immune to it. The amount of exposure to sun, wind, and salt water; the diet; and changes in blood chemistry are thought to be concerned with a person's susceptibility, as well as the amount of the potent sap encountered.

An Abundant, Widespread Plant

Since poison ivy in some form or

Poison ivy has leaves in groups of three

Poison sumac has grayish-white berries that hang downward

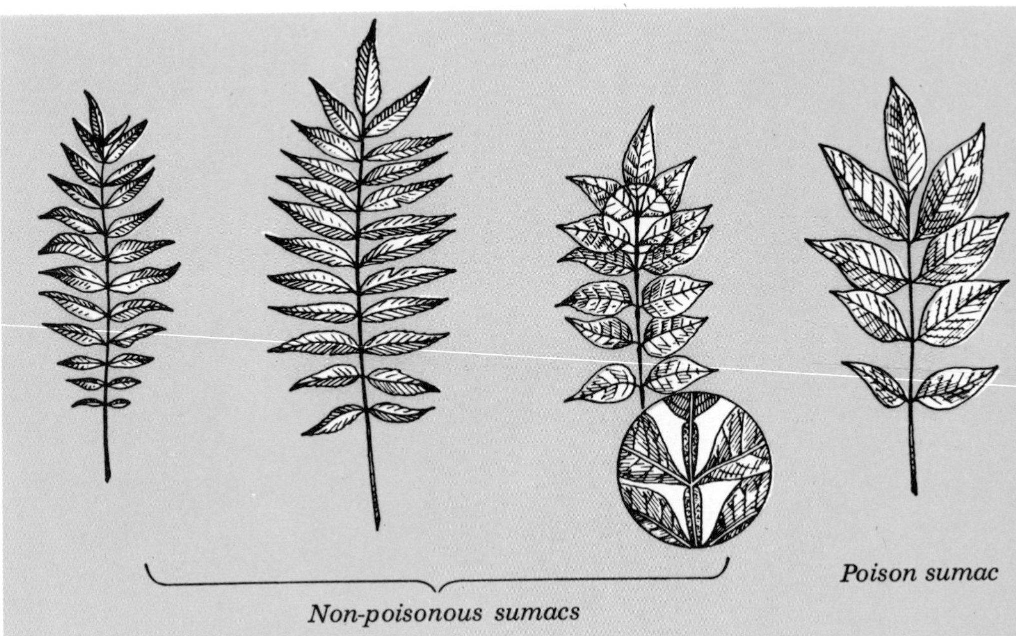

The leaves of four common sumacs are pictured here. The three to the left—smooth, staghorn, and dwarf sumacs—are entirely harmless. Only one of these three, dwarf sumac, has broad leaflets that resemble the poisonous form shown on the right. The dwarf sumac, however, has a wing along the midrib between the leaflets (circled insert). The leaves of ash trees are similar to those of poison sumac but ash tree leaves grow opposite each other along the twigs, while those of poison sumac are alternate

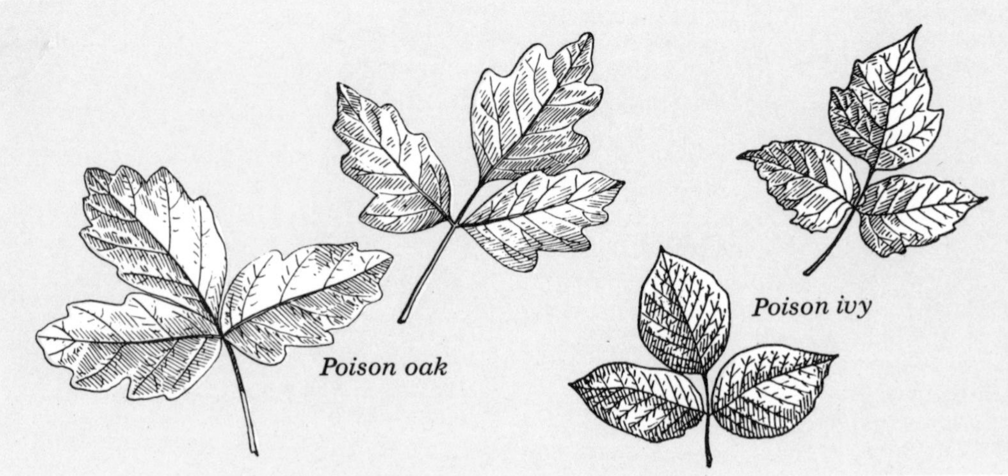

Poison ivy has a compound leaf composed of three leaflets. The leaves grow alternately on the stem of the plant. The leaflets vary greatly in shape, the two most common being pictured above. The leaf margins of poison oak are lobed rather than toothed or entire. The plant is equally poisonous, very similar, and closely related to poison ivy

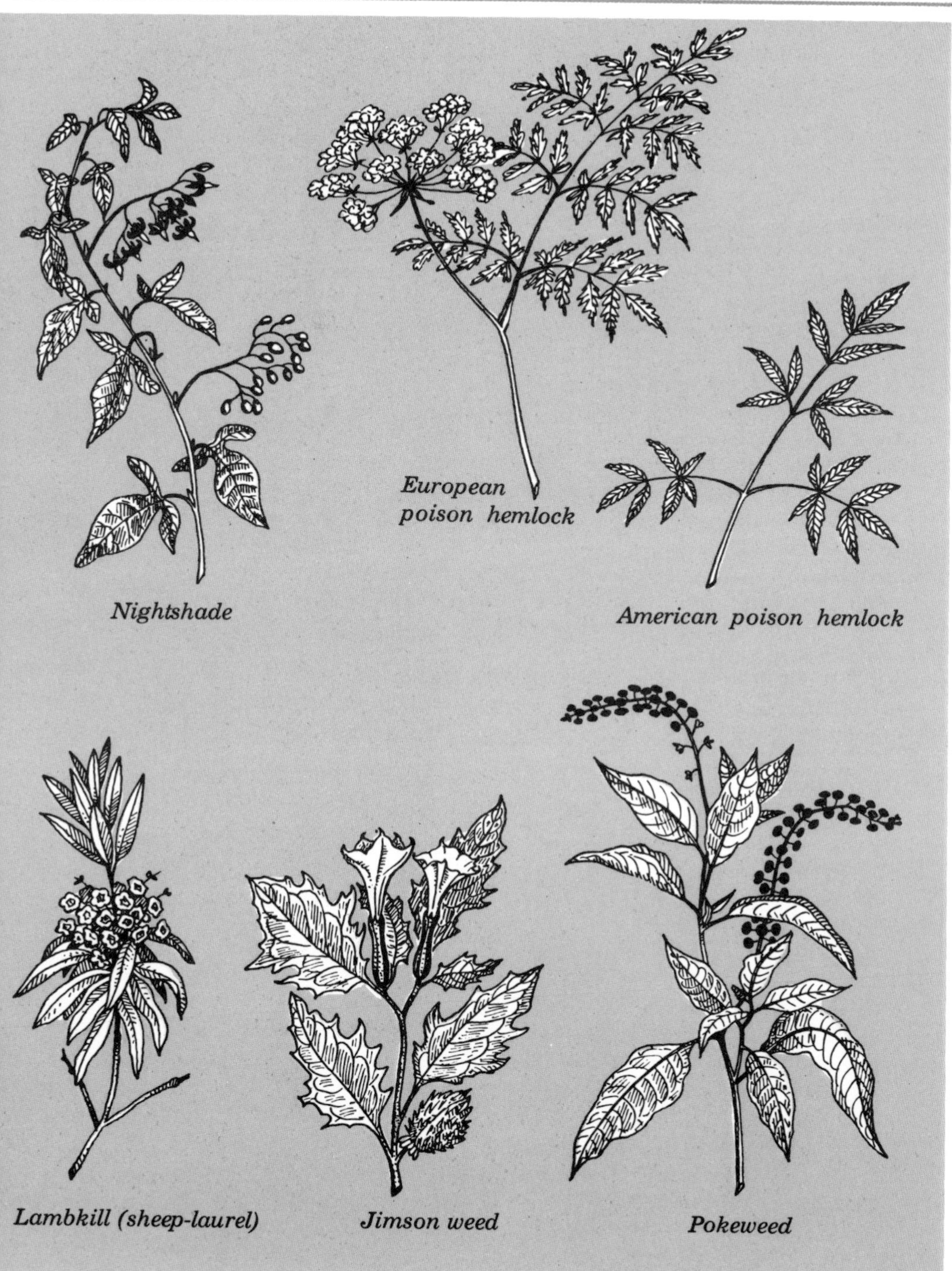

Plants that are poisonous to eat are more likely to affect grazing animals than human beings. However, one who does eat wild plants should be sure beyond any doubt that he recognizes the plant at hand and knows it to be edible. Some typical poisonous plants are illustrated above

variety is widespread throughout much of North America, one must ever be on the alert to avoid it. It thrives in sunny places—along the beaches, in overgrown pastures, upon stone walls and hedgerows. It thrives in light shade—among plantings of pine trees near reservoirs, and in parks. Even the garden fence may harbor this green plague. The dense shade of hemlock, spruce, and hardwood forests spells doom to the plants, but in openings created by fallen trees and lumbering operations, poison ivy vines flourish. Its prevalence in part may be due to the fact that some sixty kinds of birds are known to eat its fruit, thus distributing the seeds far and wide.

Contrary to common notion, sensitive persons do not become poisoned just by standing near the "itch plants." Contact with any part of the plant or with clothing and shoes that have bruised the foliage, may carry tiny drops of the irritating fluid to the human skin. Likewise, a pet dog or cat that has run through a patch of poison ivy may carry the poison on its fur. Smoke from burning brush or firewood that includes ivy vines carries minute droplets that can cause severe skin poisoning.

Fortunately, it is not hard to identify. It has compound leaves with *three* leaflets on each leaf stalk. The *middle* leaflet grows on a longer stalk than the ones on either side. Depending chiefly on the amount of light it receives, the foliage varies greatly in size, shape, color, and luster. In shade, the leaves may be thin, broad, and dull, and in extreme shade, each leaflet is narrowed and exceedingly thin. In full sun, as on the sands behind bathing beaches, the leaves become thick and glossy. But glossy leaves covered with roadside dust become dull looking again.

In the early spring the young leaves of poison ivy are purplish. In autumn their gay colors, yellow, red, and orange, may lead one who does not know the plant to gather the colorful leaves for decorations. Ivy leaves may have a jagged outline with very coarse notches, or only a single notch on a whole leaflet; other leaflets may be entire, with margins curving smoothly from base to tip.

Not all three-leaved plants are poisonous. Sometimes trillium, young jack-in-the-pulpit, and even raspberry are mistaken for poison ivy, but careful observation will show that they are quite different.

Poison ivy, which usually grows as a trailing vine, may also grow bushlike, especially near salt water, sometimes growing on erect stems 10 or more feet tall. Often it climbs trees to heights of 50 or even 75 feet above the ground, giving a tree the appearance of producing nothing but poison ivy leaves and berries.

The climbing stems of ivy are covered with numerous slender, kinky brown footlets, very slightly thickened at their tips. The harmless five-leaved Virginia creeper, or woodbine, which is often confused with poison ivy, climbs by means of tendrils similar to those of a grapevine, instead of with aerial rootlets. They are few in number and bear nearly circular adhesive disks where the tips come in contact with a wall, tree trunk, or other support. Of course, Virginia creeper is easily identified, by the five leaflets branching from the leaf stalk, instead of three as on poison ivy. Each leaflet generally has a saw-toothed margin. At the Audubon Centers (*see Nature Center*) children are told: "You can shake hands with five fingers, but not with three."

The name poison oak is frequently used interchangeably with poison ivy, but botanists limit this name to plants in the southeastern states (north to New Jersey and Missouri) and in the West to those whose leaves are distinguished by rounded lobed leaflets rather than jagged pointed ones.

Two Types of Sumacs

Poison sumac, or swamp sumac, grows in wooded swamps and along the borders of ponds and streams. A tall shrub or slender tree, it has long compound leaves, each with a row of pale green leaflets on either side of the usually red-ribbed leaf stalks. The branching clusters of small greenish-white flowers resemble the bloom of poison ivy so closely that botanists are agreed the two plants must be closely related. The grayish-white berries *hang down* when ripe.

In contrast, the harmless, red-berried sumacs grow in dry places, often along roadways and in abandoned fields. The red fruit-clusters grow on *erect* stalks.

Poison sumac is especially dangerous because the out-doors-man whose attention is drawn to fish or bird may not realize he is brushing against the shoulder-high foliage with face and arms. This too is doubtless widely distributed by birds; at least 16 species are known to eat the fruit.

Poison ivy, poison oak, and poison sumac all belong to the cashew, or sumac, family and all are in the same genus, *Rhus* (*See Sumac*). The poisonous substance or principle of the three is a yellowish, slightly volatile oil, urushiol, one of the phenols. It occurs in the sap and is present in the leaves, flowers, fruits, bark, stem, and roots of the plant.

Persons who cannot avoid contact with ivy find it helpful to make a lather of wet, yellow laundry soap and spread it as a protective film over the most exposed parts of the body – the face, hands, arms, and legs, particularly the wrists, fingers, and ankles – before going into the field. The more completely this film coats the skin the better the chance that the irritating oil will be washed away with the dissolving soap when one bathes after contact with the plant.

Treatment for Ivy Poisoning

Thorough soaping, preferably with a lather of yellow laundry soap, within the first half hour *after* exposure to poison ivy may avert poisoning. The sooner this is done the more effective it is because the oily sap of poison ivy dries quickly on one's skin. For years the standard remedy available in all drug stores has been calamine, with or without phenol. It temporarily relieves the intense itching. Recently very effective new ointments of the vanishing-cream type have appeared. They contain zirconium (a metal with many industrial uses), which not only stops the itching and burning, but in some cases has caused the blisters to dry up within 24 hours. Immediate use of zirconium-type ointments may even prevent blistering because the material combines with and neutralizes the poison.

Extracts from poison ivy have been prescribed for injection or to be taken by mouth but, until recently, without notable success. Poison ivy pills were introduced in 1959 and because of the ease of treatment were widely used. Most persons reported that complete immunity was achieved or that any rash that developed was short-lived and not troublesome. A few persons developed severe side reactions or attacks of ivy poisoning, it has been reported. Therefore, as with most other medication, the pills should be taken under a physician's supervision.

In the absence of drugstore preparations, country folks have long used the alkaline juices of certain herbs, particularly jewelweed (*Impatiens*) and both the common and Rugel's plantain (*Plantago*). Saltwater bathing has been found soothing to many, partly because of the alkaline reaction of seawater and the drying action when the salt water evaporates on the skin. Wet dressings using mild salt solution, boric acid, or diluted potassium permanganate are recommended. But with the new, more promising treatments now available it is wise for persons who are subject to frequent, severe poisoning to consult a doctor at the first sign of trouble.

Other Precautions

Since the active substance in the poison ivy plant is nonvolatile at ordinary temperatures, it may remain on clothing, furs, and shoes for some time after extensive contact with the plants. Outer clothing should be dry-cleaned to prevent recurrent attacks. Underclothing and socks should be washed in sudsy warm water and thoroughly rinsed. Shoes should be cleaned with leather-soap lather, dried and polished.

Dogs that have run through ivy-covered territory should be bathed in thick suds lest persons with sensitive skins be poisoned when they fondle their pets.

How to Kill Poison Ivy

On bathing beaches, along heavily traveled paths and in gardens, judicious and timely use of a spray containing ammonium sulfamate, such as Ammate (DuPont) or Amino Triazole (Dow), will eradicate poison ivy. The plants should be sprayed in sunny, hot weather until wet but not dripping. The leaves wilt within 24 hours and die within a week or two. Any new leaves that appear should be sprayed after about one month. Under no circumstances should it be used by persons who are not familiar with the different kinds of weeds and ornamental plants because virtually everything except grass is killed by the spray.

When poison ivy is interwined with valuable decorative plants it may be destroyed by painting the stems (pare the bark off a three-foot long section near the base if stem is more than a third of an inch thick) with a paste made for this particular purpose. One's own can be mixed by using cheap axle grease, or a hydrogenated vegetable oil such as Crisco, and mixing with a brush killer such as Esteron (Dow) or Pittsburgh's Brush Killer No. 2. Mix nine parts of the grease with one part of the chemical. Within a few weeks the ivy will be dead.

Other Plants Toxic to the Skin

While poison ivy, oak, and sumac are the best known plants that cause severe inflammation and blistering of the skin, there are numerous others. In southern Florida, including the Keys, much distress if caused by contact with poisonwood, *Metopium toxiflorum,* and with the manchineal tree, *Hippomana manchinella,* both small trees with milky juice.

The greenhouse primrose, *Primula obsconica,* will produce an itching rash on the hands and arms of many persons who handle the plants. The familiar snow-on-the-mountain, frequently grown as a border plant in gardens and which grows wild in many parts of the country, contains a toxic milky juice.

Plants Poisonous When Eaten

Other more dangerous plants, also common, are those that cause poisoning when eaten by humans or cattle. The "cup that killed Socrates" was probably brewed from *Conium maculatum,* the poison hemlock of Europe. It is now well established in this country. Native water hemlock, or spotted cowbane, *Cicuta maculata,* also is poisonous. Its flat-topped or slightly convex clusters of tiny white flowers remind one of the related, but harmless, Queen Anne's lace, or wild carrot. The poisonous water hemlock is, of course, quite unlike the familiar evergreen hemlock tree and the popular use of the name hemlock in both cases is a coincidence.

Water hemlock grows plentifully in ditches along roadsides, in pasture fields, borders of swamps and streams, wet meadows, and thickets, always in wet or poorly drained spots. Its poisonous qualities were known by the American Indians. Among the Iroquois or Five Nations it was called the "suicide plant."

The familiar pokeweed (*Phytolacca*) of clearings and woods borders produces a luxuriant growth of juicy purple berries in the fall. Although the large root is poisonous, the *young shoots* of the plant are sometimes eaten as potherbs but only after thorough cooking during which the first water is discarded. The seeds in the fleshy black fruit also are poisonous. This seems surprising since they are a favorite food of thrushes and many other birds. The explanation seems to be that the birds' digestion of the fruit is so rapid that the seeds are eliminated in the droppings before doing any harm.

Fruit of the European bittersweet, *Solanum dulcamara,* or red-berried nightshade, is poisonous. It should not be confused with the unrelated Oriental bittersweet nor with the American climbing bittersweet, *Celastrus scandens,* both of which have orange colored husks covering scarlet fruits.

Wilted cherry leaves and even wilted cherry blossoms may contain prussic acid for a period until they are entirely dried. Persons who keep horses and those who enjoy riding them must be particularly careful not to allow horses to browse on broken branches of cherry trees containing even a few wilted leaves. Veterinarians and chemists are well aware of the dangerous results of such a diet.

Litters of pigs have been poisoned at times by eating small green seedlings of cocklebur, a common barnyard weed. Oddly enough, the cocklebur is not poisonous after it has grown beyond the early seedling stage in which the first pair of seed leaves, or cotyledons, appear to contain an active poison. Hungry sheep, too, have died after browsing on the tender shoots of a narrow-leaved and small-flowered species of laurel appropriately called lambkill. For some unexplained reason, well-fed browsing and grazing animals seem to avoid instinctively most poisonous plants, and a goat, no matter how hungry, will shun mayapple leaves, jimsonweed (*Datura*), and a number of other plants that contain active poisons.

Milk sickness in humans and trembles in cattle were traced many years ago to the white snakeroot, generally eaten in late summer when pastures were dry and green feed scarce. Modern dairy farmers grow crops of mixed grasses and legumes which they can use when pastures fail.

It is possible here to mention only a few of the plants that are poisonous when eaten. Books under *Recommended Reading* will tell more about them. Muenscher's *Poisonous Plants* describes some four hundred. While many of them are common near homes one need not be concerned unless he makes a practice or hobby of eating wild plants. In that case a person must be able to recognize beyond any possible doubt the plants collected and know that each is harmless (*See also under Amanita and under Fungus*).

The annoyance and misery caused by poisonous plants has been endured with resignation for untold ages. Now that there are means for alerting everyone to their hazards, and promising new treatments for those affected by these plants, there is little reason to be seriously inconvenienced by them any longer.

—R.B.G. and C.H.M.

Recommended Reading

Edible Wild Plants of Eastern North America—Merritt L. Fernald and Alfred C. Kinsey. Idlewild Press, Cornwall, New York.

How to Kill Poison Ivy and Poison Oak—*Consumer Reports*, August 1956.

Poison Ivy—E.G. Anderson. Publication 820, Circular 180. Science Service, Dominion Department of Agriculture, Ottawa, Canada.

Poison Ivy—Health Information Series No. 65. Public Health Service, U.S. Department of Health, Education and Welfare, Washington 25, D.C

Poison Ivy and Poison Oak—William M. Harlow. N.Y. State College of Forestry, Syracuse, New York.

Poison Ivy, Poison Oak and Poison Sumac: Identification, Precautions, Eradication—Donald M. Crooks and Leonard W. Kephart. Farmers' Bulletin No. 1972, U.S. Department of Agriculture. Government Printing Office, Washington 25, D.C.

Poisonous Plants of the United States—Walter C. Muenscher. The Macmillan Company, New York.

That Scourge of Summer: Poison Ivy—Albert Q. Maisel. *Readers Digest*, August 1958.

The Venus' flytrap grows in sandy bogs. Its leaves are hinged in the middle and, when triggered, close over their prey

Some Insect-eating Plants

Green plants contain chlorophyll and are able to manufacture food for themselves in the presence of sunlight. Plants that lack chlorophyll, such as mushrooms and bacteria, obtain their food from living or dead plants and animals.

There is an interesting group of plants called carnivorous, or flesh-eating, plants that have chlorophyll that is used in the manufacture of food and, in addition, these plants have remarkable devices for capturing live insects or other small live animals. Since most of these plants capture insects chiefly, they are usually called insectivorous plants. Once an insect is captured, a digestive fluid is poured over it by the plant and this juice digests the prey. Insectivorous plants grow in bogs where the supply of nitrogen is very poor (*See Bog*). Some botanists believe that these curious plants have evolved the carnivorous habit in order to obtain nitrogen from the decomposing animal bodies.

Pitcher plants. There are several species of pitcher plants in the United States, the most common being the huntsman's horn, *Sarracenia flava,* of the South; the California pitcher plant, *Darlingtonia californica;* and our northern species, *Sarracenia purpurea.* The northern pitcher plant is a perennial marsh plant with a rosette of leaves from whose center grows a single nodding flower. The leaves are in the form of slender pitchers, each pitcher winged at one side and having a hood at the top to which insects are attracted by the bright coloring and the nectar secreted there. The interior of the pitcher is partly filled with water and the lower part of the wall is lined with stiff, downward pointing hairs that prevent the escape of the insect. The insects that are drowned in the water decompose, and the products are absorbed by the walls of the pitcher.

The sundews (*Drosera*). The sundews are very small plants growing in marshy and swampy regions in practically all of the United States. The plants are low, with leaves growing in a rosette and each leaf bearing numerous red hairs ending in tiny red glands that exude a sticky liquid. The drops of clear liquid appear like dew on the leaves. An insect alighting upon the leaf becomes entangled in the sticky fluid and the hairs curve in and hold the insect until it is digested. Three species of sundews are found in parts of the northeastern United States: round-leaved sundew, *Drosera rotundifolia*—the round leaves form a rosette close to the ground; long-leaved sundew, *Drosera longifolia*—similar in appearance but the leaves are a long oval in shape; thread-leaved sundew, *Drosera filiformis*—the leaves are erect and threadlike.

Venus' flytrap (*Dionaea*). The Venus' flytrap is the most dramatic of all plants that capture insect prey. It is a small plant growing in sandy bogs and pine lands, largely in a few localities in North and South Carolina and neighboring states to the north and south. The leaves are so constructed that they can fold in half. Each leaf has two lobes standing at less than right angles to each other. There are stiff hairs around the margin, and upon the upper surface of each half are three prominent hairs. When these hairs are touched a second time, the leaf suddenly closes like a trap. Flies alighting on the leaf are caught and pressed between the folded halves. From special glands, juices are excreted by the Venus' flytrap, which digest certain portions of the insects which are then absorbed and used by the plant for food.

Bladderwort (*Utricularia*). This plant lives submerged in water. Among the finely divided leaves are numerous small bladders. Each little bladder has a valve-like lid that opens inward but not outward. Tiny water insects, crustaceans, and other water animals are trapped in the bladders when the inward-opening door swings back into place (*See under Bladderwort*).

Recommended Reading

Insectivorous Plants—Charles Darwin. Appleton-Century-Crofts, New York.
The World of Plant Life—C.J. Hylander. The Macmillan Company, New York.

PLANTS AND WATER FOR BIRDS

In a small garden with little or no shrubbery, an increase in birds depends almost entirely on planting and developing shrub environments. To do the most good, plantings should supply the needs of the birds throughout the year. Mulberries, serviceberries, elderberries, and other shrubs with soft fruits ripening in June and July will offer food to adults and their young; wild cherries, and the fruits of viburnums and dogwoods attract migrating flocks of birds in late summer and early fall; birches and other seed-bearing trees provide food during shortages in late winter and early spring (*See under Hedgerow*).

One should be careful not to plant every patch of open ground in the yard, observing a well-known biological rule that recognizes that extensive growths of any one kind of plant do not produce a maximum of bird species. It is the interspersed, mixed plantings of trees, shrubs, herbs, and grasses—plantings that have shrubs meeting woodlands or openings of grass and other vegetation—that attract the greatest varieties of birds and other wild creatures. Two- to three-foot high deciduous shrubs may be planted about three feet apart to assure a dense ground cover from the start. One should be careful to put only the kinds of plants in the shaded places that are assured of growing there, reserving the sunny places for those species that require plenty of light. Plantings, if spotted in clusters at the edges of the lawn, leave grassy places for robins, chipping sparrows, and catbirds. Most of these shrub clumps have some evergreens planted in them to make winter shelter for birds and to offer them escape cover into which they may plunge when a hawk or shrike appears.

Where to Buy the Plants

Planting stock may be ordered from both state and privately owned nurseries, wherever one can get healthy, native species with abundant fruiting qualities. Native plants are not always necessary, if one is sure that the fruits of certain exotic species are acceptable to birds. Some nurserymen have observed which fruits birds seek and can recommend for planting the introduced species that birds prefer.

Some nurseries have "cull" plants which may be cheaper to buy, although lower cost should not always influence the choice of planting stock. The more expensive, but good, healthy plants, are cheaper in the long run in preference to less expensive and sickly stock which may not survive. Trees for reforestation are usually cheaper to buy in state-owned nurseries, some of which raise shrubs and other plants whose fruits or seeds attract wildlife.

Twelve Pairs of Birds an Acre

How much can bird species be increased in the backyard? The theoretical limit may be reached when every

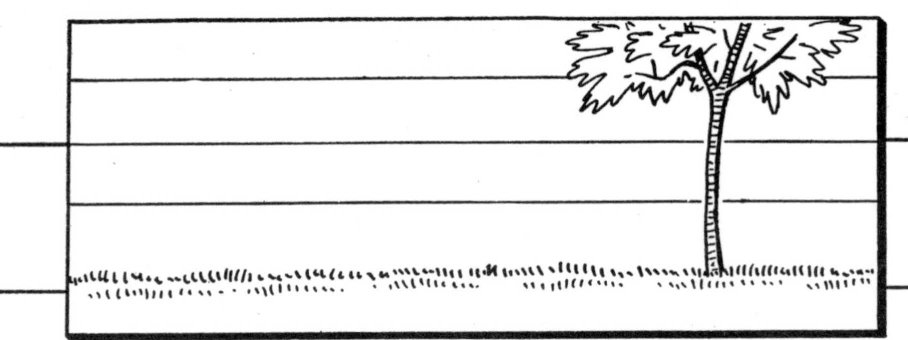

Some birds that nest in tree-trunks and hollow branches:
Woodpeckers, crested flycatcher, bluebird, sparr hawk, screech owl, chickadee, tufted titmouse, starlir

Some birds that nest in higher bushes and saplings:
Yellow- and black-billed cuckoos, yellow warbler, chipping sparrow, mourning dove, goldfinch, cedar waxwing, kingbird.

Some birds that nest in low bushes:
Field sparrow, song sparrow, chestnut-sided warbler, catbird, cardinal, brown thrasher

Some birds that nest on the ground:
Ovenbird, black and white warbler, junco, veery, towhee, bob-white quail, whip-poor-will.

available nesting site for every local kind of bird has been created. Planting trees, shrubs, and vines, and erecting birdhouses and birdbaths will attract birds to a yard and *make them satisfied to stay there.* On the 12-acre Roosevelt Bird Sanctuary at Oyster Bay, Long Island, the National Audubon Society, through balanced planting and protection, increased birds from a few breeding species each year to 145 breeding pairs of *30 different* kinds, or about 12 nesting pairs on each acre. This is exceptionally high compared to most woodland bird populations of about two pairs an acre and it has been achieved on a fair-sized tract of land. But a wide *variety* of birds is not an impossible goal for people whose yards have only an acre of ground or less.

Experience with Other Wildlife Plantings

During an eight-year period the United States Soil Conservation Service planted more than 20 million trees, shrubs, and vines for erosion control and wildlife conservation on farms in the northeastern states. Early in the planting experience they discovered that nursery-grown trees, shrubs, and vines were superior to wild plants dug in the field and then transplanted to farms. Nursery stock from the Soil Conservation Service's own nurseries not only survived better, but fruited more consistently and bore a heavier crop. Also it was found that spring plantings usually survived better than fall plantings, perhaps because of greater soil moisture in spring and the generally cooler temperatures.

NESTING HEIGHTS OF VARIOUS KINDS OF BIRDS

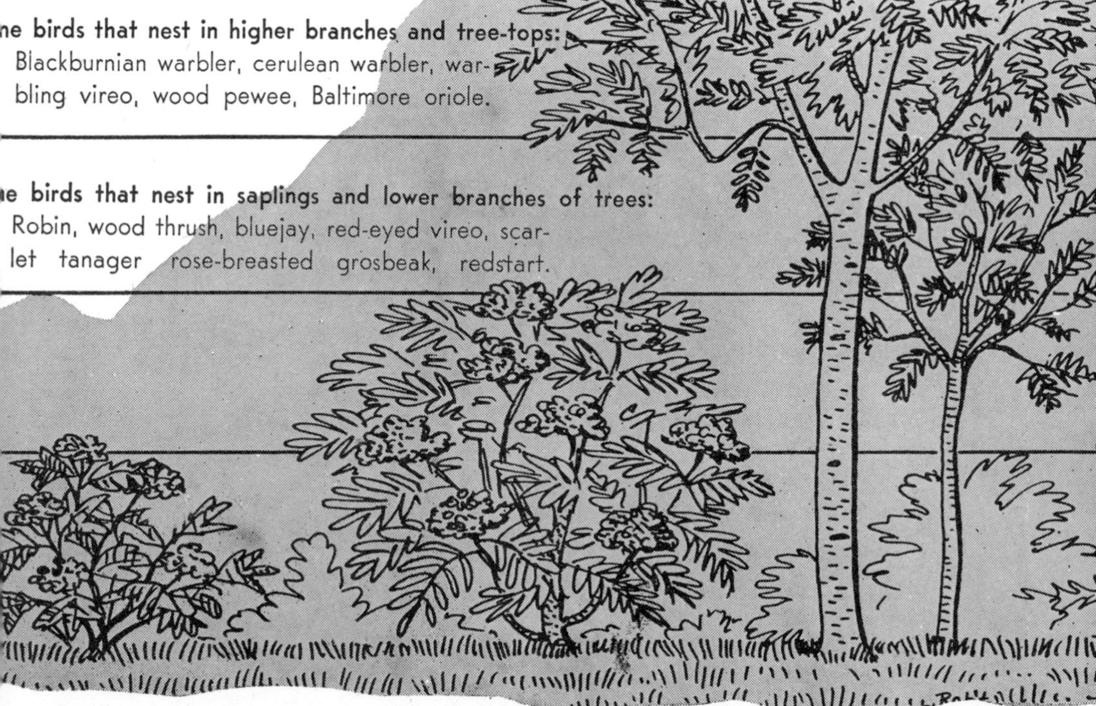

By providing vegetation of various heights, the number of species of birds nesting in an area can be greatly increased

Blueberry

Red cedar

Viburnum

Black cherry

Blackberry

Wildlife plantings, made in eroded gullies, or planted as soil-conserving hedgerows, and borders along eroded, open woodlands, were either native plants, or hardy introduced species. The plants considered as most successful were those which survived on poor, dry soils, and also yielded fine crops of fruit. Some of those producing fruits and cover for birds and other kinds of wildlife were: coralberry, *Symphoricarpos orbiculatus;* bayberry, *Myrica carolinensis;* European mountain ash, *Sorbus aucuparia;* silky cornel, *Cornus ammomum;* American hazelnut, *Corylus americana;* Tatarian honeysuckle, *Lonicera tatarica;* Multiflora rose, *Rosa multiflora;* highbush cranberry, *Viburnum trilobum;* and Virginia creeper, *Parthenocissus quinquefolia.*

Care of Tree and Shrub Plantings

Wildlife tree and shrub plantings that are allowed to grow uncontrolled may, within 10 or 15 years, outgrow their usefulness. Some plants grow swiftly and, where crowded together, are usually highly competitive. Unless they are managed, woody plants will grow into a veritable backyard jungle, with the shade-tolerant shrubs and small trees eventually topping and crowding out those which require plenty of sunlight.

Use a pair or pruning shears and a small handsaw at least once a year to cut back or thin out some of the more vigorous-growing plants. In this way not only is the backyard kept neater, but the plants which continue to provide varied foods and nesting sites for birds are controlled.

Birds and Water

Spring and summer droughts underline the great need that birds have for water. As important to them as food and cover in the backyard, water is not only life-giving, but, when present, will prevent birds from flying long distances away from the garden to get it. A robin running across a parched lawn, with its mouth open, or a mourning dove peering wistfully into a dried-up pool, are signs of creatures that are mutely crying out for a drink of clear, cool water. Not only do they need water for drink-

Oregon grape

ing, but birds also enjoy bathing frequently, especially during the hot, dry months of the year.

Birdbaths, or drinking places, are not difficult to make. They vary from the simplicity of a shallow pan filled with water and placed in the ground, to the ornate, sculptured birdbaths in formal gardens of large estates. One feature all of them should have in common: They should range in depth from about one-half an inch to no more than two or three inches at their deepest part. Birds are afraid of deep water and when bathing along a stream's edge, or in a woodland pool, they seek the shallows and small trickles of water over rocks and other places in which to flutter.

—J.K.T.

Recommended Reading

Handbook of Attracting Birds – Thomas P. McElroy, Jr. Alfred A. Knopf, New York.

Songbirds in Your Garden – John K. Terres. Thomas Y. Crowell Company, New York.

PLANT LICE (*See under Aphid; also under Lacewing*)

BUILD IT YOURSELF

Ground level birdbaths may be made by pouring a slab of concrete into a scooped-out depression two or three feet in diameter. Mixture: 4 parts sand or gravel to one of cement. Mix thoroughly with hoe and add water until mix flows evenly.

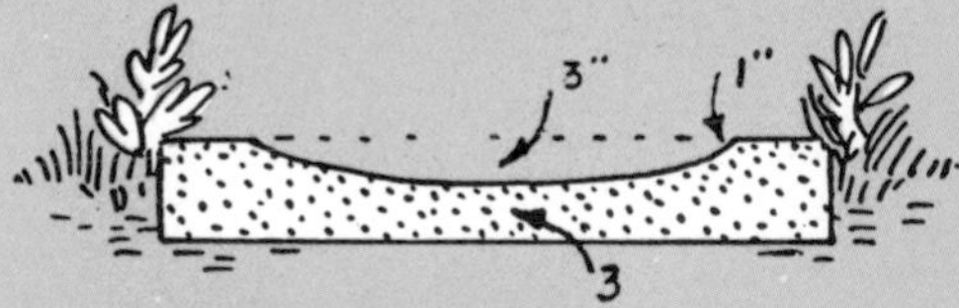

Running water attract birds. Water dripping into the birdbath from a bucket (below) with a small hole in the bottom will attract shyer woodland birds.

For unique birdbaths, chip one in a flat-topped rock (above) or pour cement into a depression in a pile of arranged boulders (below).

A shell of the giant clam. *Tridacna gigas,* makes a novel birdbath (below). Large shells of this species can be used on the ground, or mounted on a stump or rock.

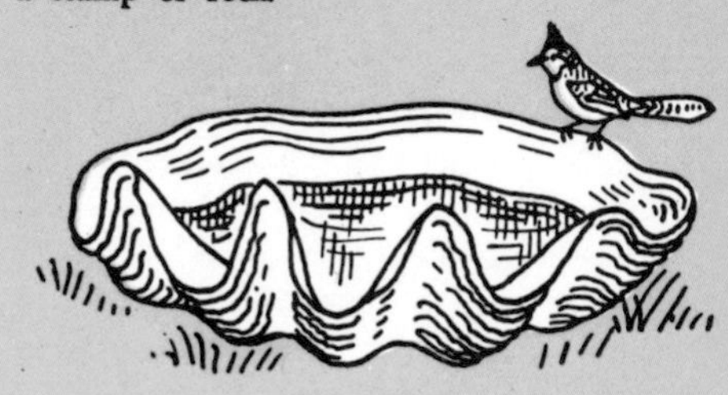

An American golden plover stands near its nest—a slight depression lined with mosses and lichens

PLOVER

Among the smaller wading birds, larger and more plump than most sandpipers and smaller than curlews and godwits, the plovers are shorebirds with short bills. They rarely wade, but run along the margin of oceans, rivers, and ponds, pattering swiftly in short bursts of activity, stopping to seize an insect, tiny shrimp, or other animal food.

When mixed with sandpipers of various species, the plover can be identified immediately by its bill. Not only is it shorter than the length of the head, but it is slightly swollen at the tip. The head itself appears to be larger, in proportion to body size, and the neck is shorter.

In North America, five species of plover are ringed; in spring plumage they wear a black collar across their white throats. The largest of these, the killdeer, has two such collars. The killdeer breeds throughout most of North America south from British Columbia and Quebec. It feeds on insects, and is generally found in pastures, meadows, and freshly plowed fields (*See under Killdeer*).

The other ringed plovers — Wilson's semipalmated, piping, and snowy—are more often found near water. All of them are darker above than below, with backs nearly the color of the mudbanks or sandbars that they frequent. Wilson's plover, *Charadrius wilsonia,* is the largest and darkest of these, with a dark, stout bill.

The semipalmated plover, *C. semipalmatus,* is noticeably smaller, with a two-toned bill and yellowish legs. These birds occur together only in the range of the Wilson's plover—along the Mexican coast on the Pacific and south of Virginia on the Atlantic; the semipalmated plover breeds in the Arctic, wintering from the Carolinas and central California south.

The piping and the snowy plovers, *C. melodus,* and *C. alexandrinus,* are gray, rather than brown, on backs and heads. The snowy plover has yellow legs; the piping plover's legs are black. In both species, the collar is not always complete, and is reduced to faint shoulder markings in winter. The piping plover breeds inland in the northern United States and southern Canada, and along the Atlantic Coast south to Virginia; the snowy plover, along the Pacific Coast from Washington south to Baja California, and east through Colorado, Kansas, and the Southwest to north-central Texas.

The mountain plover, *Eupoda montana,* is an inland bird in summer, from Montana to Texas, in sagebrush and short-grass prairie. It has no collar, and its plumage is dull, a grayish-brown above and white below. It winters from central California, and southern Arizona east to Texas along the Gulf Coast and south to Mexican shores.

The two largest plovers in North America are the very similar black-bellied plover, *Squatarola squatarola,* and the American golden plover, *Pluvialis dominica.* Both are grayish above and black below in spring, with a yellow wash on the back of the American golden plover; this species has its black underparts extending to the tail and also white on the rump. Even in the dull winter plumage, when the black on the underside has completely vanished, the black-bellied plover has a tuft of black feathers under the wing (axillars) where the American golden plover is completely white. The golden plover migrates north through the center of the continent to breed in the Arctic, then flies south in the fall well offshore in the Atlantic to winter from Brazil to Argentina. The black-bellied plover breeds in the same region, but winters from British Columbia and New Jersey south to Brazil; most individuals migrate along the coasts, with a few following the inland route.

—G.B.S.

Wilson's plover nests on the open beach just above the tide line

In fall, the black breast plumage of the black-bellied plover is replaced with white feathers

Hunted for its plumage, the American golden plover was nearly extinct 60 years ago

Black-bellied plover
Other Common Names—Beetlehead
Scientific Name—*Squatarola squatarola*
Family—Charadriidae (plovers, turnstones, and surfbirds)
Order—Charadriiformes
Size—Length, 11½ inches
Range—Arctic in the summer: from New Jersey and British Columbia south in winter

American Golden Plover
Other Common Names—Squealer, rainbird
Scientific Name—*Pluvialis dominica*
Family—Charadriidae (plovers, turnstones, and surfbirds)
Order—Charadriiformes
Size—Length, 10½ inches
Range—Breeds in the Arctic; winters in South America

The mountain plover spends its summers in dry, short-grass prairies. When danger threatens, it prefers to run away on its long legs. Forced to fly, it stays close to the ground

Mountain Plover
Other Common Names—Prairie plover
Scientific Name—*Eupoda montana*
Family—Charadriidae (plovers, turnstones, and surf birds)
Order—Charadriiformes
Size—Length, 9¼ inches
Range—Breeds from northern Montana and occasionally northeastern North Dakota south through eastern Wyoming, western Nebraska, eastern Colorado, and western Kansas to central eastern New Mexico and western Texas. In winter south from central California to southern Arizona, the Texas coast to southern Baja California

POCKET GOPHER *(See under Gopher)*

POCKET MOUSE *(See under Mouse; and under Rodent)*

POINT REYES NATIONAL SEASHORE

Location—Coast of California
Size—53,000 acres
Mammals—Deer, foxes, rodents, seals
Birdlife—Gulls, terns, shorebirds, songbirds
Plants—Mountain forests, shore vegetation, grasslands

This national seashore extends along the coast for 28 miles and reaches back through rolling grasslands country to high, rugged mountains. It contains desolate valleys of broken rocks and caves, sea cliffs, open beaches, and sandpits. About 26,000 acres are cattle range, and will be maintained as such.

POISON IVY *(See under Plant: Poison Ivy and Other Poisonous Plants)*

POLLEN

The male sex cells, the microspores, of the seed plants are called pollen. Formed in the anthers at the tip of the stamens, pollen is usually yellow, but may be white, red, or blue. It is always very fine, and the word comes from the Latin for *dustlike.*

In order to carry on the next generation of plants of its species, pollen must be transported from the anther to an ovary of a plant of the same species. With some plant families, pollen from a flower falls on the female part of the same flower, and self-pollination occurs. Cross-pollinization is more frequent; the pollen grains are carried by the wind, by birds and insects, or in the case of the few flowering plants that have be-

Point Reyes National Seashore extends for 28 miles along the California coast

come completely aquatic, by water. Wind-pollinated flowes are usually very numerous and produce clouds of pollen. Insect-pollinated flowers are fewer, and more likely to be colorful and scented.

Each pollen grain consists of two cells. Once the grain has landed on the stigma, the pollen-receiving structure of the female part of the flower, the outer cell grows down the stigma and into the ovary. The other cell moves through this channel and into the ovary, where it fertilizes the female cell within.

Each species of plant has a distinctive pollen grain. The study of the various shapes is a specialized branch of botany, and one that has considerable application in determining the past distribution of plants by identifying fossilized pollen grains. (*See also under Pollination*)

—G.B.S.

POLLINATION

Insects and Pollination

Many people think of insects as animals to be swatted, stepped on, or otherwise liquidated at every opportunity, and refer to them as "bugs." They think of the damage done by insects, and look upon any animal which destroys them as beneficial. But such people see only one side of the picture. *Actually, less than one percent of all the insects can be considered pests*. Not only are the insects exceedingly interesting animals, but many of them are highly beneficial to man. Human society would not exist in its present form without them.

Insects benefit man directly or indirectly in many ways, one of the most important being the pollination of plants. Without pollination by insects there would be few vegetables, few fruits, little or no clover (and hence much less beef, mutton, and wool), no cotton or linen, no coffee, no tobacco, few flowers —in fact, a great many of the things that are an integral part of the domestic economy and civilization would be nonexistent without the services of insects (*See under Insect*).

Pollination

In the higher plants the male germ cells (the pollen) are produced on the stamens of the flowers, and the female germ cells are formed in the ovary. Before fertilization can take place a pollen grain must get from a stamen to the stigma and work its way down the style to the female germ cell (*See under Pollen*). This transfer of pollen and fertilization must take place in practically every case before the flower will set seed. As the seed develops, the tissues around it swell and form the fruit.

The relationships between insects and flowers that result in pollination are among the most interesting, and from man's point of view among the most important, of all natural phenomena. A few of the higher plants are self-pollinating, but the majority are cross-pollinated, that is, the pollen of one flower is transferred to the stigma of another. Cross-pollination may be necessary to the continued vigor of the plant, or the flower's structure may be such that self-pollination is impossible.

Pollen is transferred from one plant to another in two principal ways, by the wind and by insects and by some species of birds. Wind-pollinated plants (pines for example) produce a large amount of dry pollen that is blown all over the landscape. Such plants survive because a few of the millions of pollen grains produced happen to land on the stigma of the right flower. Insect-pollinated plants produce smaller amounts of pollen that is usually sticky and adheres to the bodies of insects that visit the flowers. This pollen is later rubbed off accidentally by the insect onto the stigma of another flower.

In general, the plants that are wind-pollinated have flowers that are small, inconspicuous, and weakly scented, while those that are insect-pollinated tend to have larger, more conspicuous, and strongly scented flowers. It is sometimes said that insect-pollinated plants develop these characteristics in order to attract insects and insure pollination; however, this idea is, in part, based on the entirely unwarranted assumption that a plant has intelligence enough to figure the whole thing out and the ability to develop the needed characteristics. Evolutionists do not feel this way but believe that these adaptations have been shaped by evolution, or slow modifications in response to environmental pressures, or possibly as a result of mutations. However, many plants that are not pollinated by insects, such as the conifers, may have rich nectar of highly scented flowers, and many insect-pollinated plants have inconspicuous flowers or produce no nectar.

Special Relationships Between Plants and Insects

Many flowers have peculiar features of structure that help to insure pollination. Some, such as the iris, are so constructed that an insect cannot get to the nectar without collecting pollen on its body, and cannot enter the next flower of this same kind without leaving some of this pollen at the stigma of that flower. Milkweeds have special pollen masses, the pollina, that are arranged so that when an insect alights on the edge of the flower its legs slip into a fissure in the pollinia; the pollinia then become attached to the insect's leg and are carried to the next flower.

Some plants are dependent upon a single species or type of insect for pollination. Some of the orchids are pollinated only by certain long-tongued hawk moths. The Smyrna fig is pollinated by the fig wasp, *Blastophaga psenes,* and the yucca is pollinated solely by the yucca moth, *Tegeticula alba* (*See Joshua Tree*). The Smyrna fig is peculiar in that all its flowers are female and produce no pollen; the pollen must come from a type of wild fig called the caprifig, which produces pollen but not edible fruit. The female wasp develops in a small gall at the base of the Caprifig flower, and on emerging from this gall becomes covered with Caprifig pollen; she then flies to another fig to lay her eggs, and although she lays her eggs on the Caprifig she occasionally visits the Smyrna fig and drops off enough pollen to fertilize the Smyrna fig flowers.

The larvae of the yucca moth develop on the yucca seeds, and the female moth "seems to realize" that the development of her young depends on the pollination of the flower. Before laying her eggs the moth collects pollen from a number of yucca flowers, and immediately after inserting her eggs into the ovary of a flower she places the pollen she has collected on the stigma of that flower. This insures the fertilization of the flower and the development of the seeds, and since more seeds develop than are eaten by the larvae, the perpetuation of the yucca is assured.

In most of these relationships between insects and flowers, both the insect and the plant are benefited. Most of the flower frequenting insects feed on the nectar or the pollen of the flower, and the plant seeds are fertilized. In a few cases the insect may obtain nectar from the plant without pollinating it; bumblebees, for example, often reach the nectar by cutting through the base of the corolla (petals) from the outside. Insects that feed on milkweed sometimes lose a leg in the pollinia, or are trapped and unable to escape.

Adaptations of Insect Pollinators

Many of the insects that frequent flowers have special structures that enable them to collect pollen. The body and legs of bees and some flies are covered with branched hairs to which the pollen sticks when the insect brushes against the stamens of a flower. This pollen is later brushed off the hairs of the insect onto the stigma of another flower. Apparently only pollen-gathering insects have hairs of this type. In the bees some of the pollen collected is

In a cut-away yucca blossom, the larvae and adults of the pronuba moth that pollinate this plant are revealed

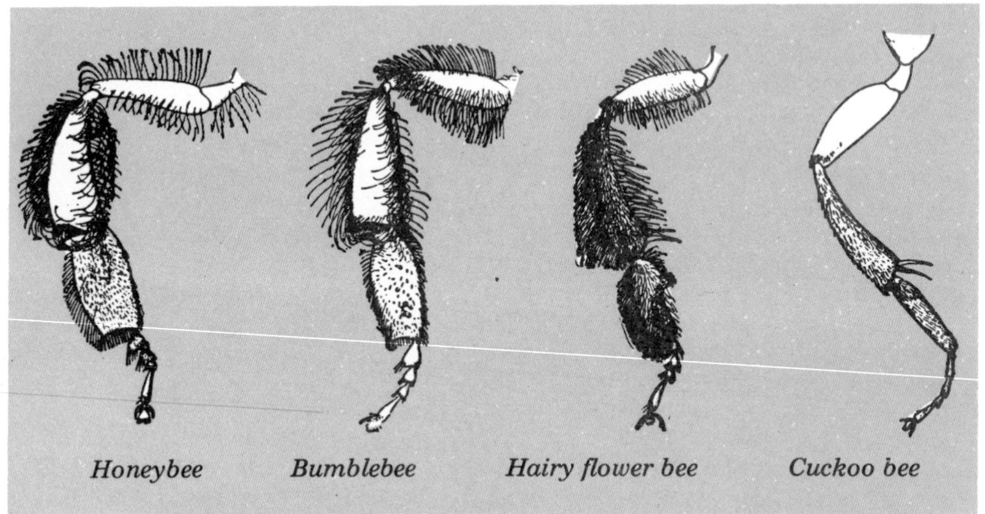

The legs of bees are equipped with short, stiff hairs, or scopa, that are used to collect pollen. Bees that are not pollen collectors, such as the cuckoo bee, that lives parasitically with other bees, lack these pollen brushes

The hawk moth is an effective pollinator of plants, especially cultivated species

The catkins of shagbark hickory (above) are designed for pollination by the wind; while, the Ohio buckeye (below) has large, showy blossoms that attract insect pollinators

carried back to the hive and used as food by the young. The pollen is combed out of the hairs on which it collects by means of the pollen combs (on the inner side of the hind tarsi) and then is transferred to the pollen baskets (on the outer side of each hind tibia). Only the workers have these pollen baskets. It is not at all uncommon to observe bees with large masses of pollen on their hind legs. When a bee returns to the hive, it thrusts its hind legs into a cell and pries the masses of pollen off the pollen basket by means of a spur on the tip of its middle tibia (*See under Bee*).

Many insects that frequent flowers have long mouthparts that enable them to feed on flowers with long nectar tubes. Many of the common hawk moths have a proboscis that is 2 or 3 inches long, and one species in Madagascar has a proboscis that is 9½ inches long. Some bees also have very long tongues; one tropical species has a tongue that is longer than the body.

Plant Types and Their Pollination

The plants that are wind-pollinated and hence not dependent upon insects are such plants as the cereals—corn, wheat, rye, oats, timothy, and other grasses; many trees, including the willows, oaks, hickories, elms, poplars, birches, and conifers; and many wild plants, including the ragweeds and pigweeds. On the other hand, most of the orchard fruits, including apples, pears, plums, cherries, and citrus fruits; berries, including strawberries, raspberries, blackberries, cranberries, and grapes; vegetables, including melons, cucumbers, pumpkins, squash, eggplant, peppers, and carrots; field crops, including the clovers and alfalfa, cotton and tobacco; and many flowers are dependent upon insects for pollination.

The plants that are normally pollinated by insects can be pollinated by hand, but this is usually a tedious process and not practical on a large scale. Most growers producing such vegetables as cucumbers in greenhouses use one or more hives of bees in the greenhouse to insure pollination.

The rosaceous plants (apple, pear, cherry, blackberry) are dependent chiefly upon honeybees for pollination; the legumes (clovers and alfalfa) are dependent upon various bees, chiefly honeybees and bumblebees. Many plants with strongly scented, and conspicuous nocturnal flowers, such as honeysuckle, tobacco, and petunias, are pollinated not only by bees but by certain moths. Umbelliferous plants (carrots, parsnips) are pollinated chiefly by various flies, bees, and wasps. Pond lilies, goldenrod, and some other flowers are pollinated by bees and certain beetles.

Economic Aspects

Clover is an important farm crop in many parts of the country, being used as hay and forage, and to enrich the soil. The average annual crop of clover seed in Ohio—250,000 bushels—would plant some three million acres in clover; the acreage would yield some 4,500,000 tons of hay (worth about $90,000,000) and add about 273 million pounds of nitrogen to the soil (worth about $50,000,000). Such clovers as red clover and alsike are entirely dependent upon insects for pollination and seed production, and sweet clover and alfalfa (though somewhat self-pollinated) depend on insect pollination for profitable seed yields. The job of pollinating clover is tremendous; an acre of red clover, for example, contains about 216 million individual flowers, and every one of these flowers must be visited by an insect before it will produce seed. Under normal field conditions, about 82 percent of the job of pollinating red clover is done by honeybees, and 15 percent by bumblebees. The average seed yield of red clover and alsike in Ohio is about 1.0 and 1.6 bushels per acre, respectively. With a dense honeybee population in clover fields these yields can be increased to 4 and 8 bushels per acre,

The pollination of clover is dependent on bees such as this bumblebee

The pollinating mechanism in alfalfa blossoms deposits pollen with such force that bees learn to avoid visits to them

Many of the crops of farmlands are dependent on bees for pollination

and with maximum insect pollination they can be increased to 12 and 20 bushels per acre.

Sheep may be raised on grasses, which are wind-pollinated, but a practical sheep raiser prefers clovers. Some years ago the sheep growers in New Zealand imported red clover seed to improve their pastures. The clover grew all right, but produced no seed for the next year's crop because there were no suitable insects in New Zealand to pollinate the clover. After bumblebees were introduced into New Zealand and became established, thereby making possible the pollination of clover, there was continuous good grazing for New Zealand sheep.

With the possible exception of sour cherries and most peaches, orchard fruits are largely or entirely insect-pollinated, and this job is done chiefly by bees. Experiments involving the use of cages over orchard trees have shown that when bees are excluded from the tree when it is in bloom the set of fruit is usually less than one percent of the blooms. When a hive of bees is caged with a tree, the set of fruit is increased—in some cases to as high as 44 percent of the blooms. Such experiments would indicate that the fruit yields in orchards would be greatly increased by the use of bees. Although there are many factors that complicate the problem of orchard pollination (weather conditions at the time of blooming, the presence of suitable varieties for pollination), many growers have obtained considerably increased yields of fruit by placing hives of bees in their orchards when the trees were in bloom.

The value to man of the pollinating insects may be realized by a consideration of the list of plants that are insect-pollinated. It would be difficult to estimate this value in terms of dollars and cents, but it is certainly well above the figure of $1,250,000,000 (which represents the yearly damage by insects in this country). Of all the insects that pollinate plants, the most important by far is the honeybee. This insect is highly prized for the honey and wax it produces, but for every dollar that a beekeeper receives, $15 to $20 dollars worth of pollination services are rendered to agriculture.

In these times when the aim everywhere is increased production, studies are continually being made of ways to increase yields by the use of bees to increase pollination. It is fortunate that the honeybee, the most important of the pollinating insects, can be controlled by man; and experiments are being made in the domestication of the bumblebee (*See under Bee*). Most of us fail to realize the importance of insects in the production of fruits and vegetables and other crops. The lowly "bug" is as important to production efforts and to the national economy as it is the farmer or the industrial worker. —D. J. B.

How Science Aids Our Bees

Bees—our most important agents for the pollination of many essential crops—are killed off at an alarming rate by some of our so-called "advanced" farming techniques, when the world's bee population is already inadequate.

In many regions of the globe it has now become necessary not only to develop bee-conservation programs but also to devise better ways of making use of the bees we have, including the 20,000 species of wild bees—3,000 of them in this country—that we have so long ignored.

Hawaii, for example, is eager to find a bee that will do a better job of pollinating three of its important crops—passion fruit, lichee, and macadamia nuts. Scientists in the Soviet Union, England, France, and other European countries are trying to build into the industrious little insects a conditioned reflex that will prompt them to seek out and pollinate only those plants that are agriculturally important, by feeding them syrups heavy with the scent of, for instance, alfalfa or red clover.

The United States Department of Agriculture's attempt to breed a new strain of honeybee is but one example of the current attempt to make better use of bees. The experiment is necessary because we are faced with an acute shortage of alfalfa seed.

Our limited supply of wild bees is unable to cross-pollinate the immense acreage of this crop. Alfalfa is essential to soil-building, crop rotation programs as well as being our number one forage crop for cattle.

One possible answer is to install honeybee hives in the fields that are inadequately covered by wild bees. But here the peculiar mechanism of the alfalfa flower becomes a critical factor. Its sexual column is held down by two overlapping petals that separate when a bee works its way into the flower's throat in search of nectar. The "triggered" column then flies up, hitting the bee in the face and showering it with pollen.

This does not deter wild bees, but after a few punishing slaps, honeybees learn to insert their proboscises lower on the flower between the wing petals from which position they can get the nectar *without* tripping the pollination mechanism. An agronomist of the United States Department of Agriculture has developed a variety of alfalfa so rich in nectar and so seductive in scent that he hopes honeybees will visit it freely enough to pollinate it well even though most of their flower visits do no good.

Entomologists are trying to breed a honeybee so eager to use alfalfa pollen that it will not hesitate to take repeated pollen-laden slaps in the face. If honeybees could be induced to collect alfalfa pollen regularly, there would be no probmen, since all visits would result in pollination. In the Southwest honeybees do collect alfalfa pollen when conditions are just right but in the Northwest this is not so.

Cornell's distinguished entomologist, E.J. Dyce, was one of the first to point out that our bee population was becoming insufficient to our needs, but his warning has been largely ignored. According to George E. Bohart, this country's leading authority on wild bee pollination and head of the United States Department of Agriculture Wild Bee Pollination Investigations Branch at Logan, Utah, "We are still killing off bees, even though we need them to sustain many forms of plantlife almost as much as we need bulls and rams to perpetuate our livestock."

When we think of bees in terms of honey, as we do almost automatically, we are actually thinking of the least important aspect of their industry. In fact, of the 20,000 known bee species only two, *Apis mellifera* and *Apis molica* (a close relative in the Orient), are reliable honey producers. All the rest are important solely as pollinators.

Even *Apis mellifera* is more valuable as a pollinator than as a honey manufacturer. As the only domesticated bee, the only bee man can easily control, it can be transported to regions that are short of wild bees. In some areas more money can be made renting bee colonies to farmers than from the sale of honey. But the honeybee can never wholly take the place of the wild bee. There are too few of them in wild areas and there are several important crops which they pollinate inefficiently.

In addition to alfalfa and clover, more than 50 crops depend entirely on bees for cross-pollination or yield far more abundantly after bees have visited them. These include apples, apricots, cherries, grapes, melons, peaches, pears, plums, nine of our berry crops, asparagus, broccoli, cabbage, onions and radishes, carrots, pumpkins, buckwheat, squash, and many other staples of our diet. Bees also assist in the cross-pollination of cotton, flax, some spices and medicinal plants, and half of our flowers.

When alfalfa, which must be reseeded every two years, experienced a decline

A honeybee approaches the lip of an apple blossom

Purple alfalfa

Red clover

in seed production, the United States Department of Agriculture began a study of wild bees of the Northwest, where much of our alfalfa seed is grown. The Logan field laboratory was opened and Bohart, then a young entomologist just out of the Navy, was put in charge in 1950. His ultimate goal was to develop practical methods of bee husbandry for the region's farmers, but first he had to explore the life habits and pollination potentials of a group of bees about which virtually nothing was known. He also had to convince farmers of the need for bee conservation.

"And that hasn't been easy," he said. "Many farmers had little understanding of the role bees play in their lives."

Most farmers, for example, practice "clean-cultivation" to control weeds. This calls for the destruction of hedgerows and rail fences and the substitution of wire fencing, so that every possible inch of cultivable land can be plowed.

Areas capable of supporting weeds—railroad rights-of-way, unused pastures, roadside ditches, brush patches—are either burned over or plowed under. While this helps control weeds it never eliminates them completely. But it does destroy the home sites of wild bees that nest in or near the ground.

Since ground-nesting bees require subsurface moisture in the soil, conventional drainage and irrigation practices often destroy nesting sites by drying them up. This was strikingly demonstrated on a tract of land near Riverton, Wyoming, which was opened to homesteading in 1951.

The homesteaders were given 10 years to line their irrigation ditches with concrete, to prevent "wasteful" seepage. They were also advised to grow alfalfa. In the first seven years the better farms produced about 700 pounds of seed per acre (national average: around 162 pounds). But as more and more homesteaders finished lining their irrigation ditches, the moisture in the soil bordering the ditches steadily diminished—and as it did the vast colonies of wild bees living alongside the ditches began to die out. Eventually, the farmers in the area had to abandon alfalfa seed growing after several years of producing only 50 pounds per acre.

Spraying and dusting crops with insecticides is as deadly to bees, obviously, as it is to harmful insects (*See under Insecticide*). Bohart recalls visiting a wild bee colony the day after a plane sprayed a nearby farm.

"It was a one-acre site," he said, "yet there wasn't a spot where I could put my hat down without it covering at least 10 dead bees. All told, I suppose a million bees were poisoned."

Since there is no known way to prevent wild bees from visiting sprayed fields, untold millions of them will be killed by insecticide poisoning each year.

Wild bees are also under constant attack from a formidable array of predators. They are eaten by mice, badgers, skunks, lizards, shrews, birds, moles, and toads. Ambush bugs and crab spiders, with markings that blend into the flowers on which they lurk, trap unwary bees and drink their blood (*See Bug*).

In some countries of Europe, a velvet ant (wasp) captures bees in its vise-like jaws and squeezes them until, in their death throes, they disgorge the honey the ant is seeking. Throughout the world, dragonflies devour bees in midair. Wasps, nicknamed "bee-wolves," snatch them up, sting them, and carry them off, paralyzed, to the wasps' nests, where the nectar is squeezed out of them and eaten. Then they are stuffed, still paralyzed, into cells in the nest to be eaten by wasp larvae.

As Bohart points out, bees have a hard enough time surviving without man doing his unthinking best to exterminate them too. But the scientist is still hopeful.

"We're beginning to learn something about wild bee husbandry," he said, "how to protect them, how to increase their numbers, how to move them to places where they are needed. But just beginning."

Early in his work Bohart found that about 60 species of wild bees hovered over the Northwest's alfalfa fields. He then had to determine how important a pollinator each species was. This involved locating their nesting sites. He then kept them under observation to determing how many trips to the alfalfa fields each species made per day, and how much pollen was carried back to the nest on each trip.

This was done by plugging the mouths of a series of nests with cotton, once the bees left them. On their return, the bees had to pause to pull out the plugs. This gave Bohart a chance to count the number of round trips each bee made a day, and to check the quantity of pollen it carried on its return trips.

By a process of elimination, he chose 16 species for additional studies involving their nesting habits, the number of blossoms they visited per minute, their flight range, the architecture of their nests, and their susceptibility to insecticides.

To learn the structure of a nest he either sliced away its wall and photographed its interior, or poured plaster of Paris down a burrow and let it harden. To check their vulnerability to insecticides he had to take a sickle and cut away all the vegetation from small plots in the fields where he conducted his experiments, since bees, whenever possible, crawl into fissures in the ground to die. Then it was a tedious matter of getting down on his hands and knees and crawling over the ground, inch by inch, to count the dead.

By 1955 he had determined that of all the region's wild bees the alkali bee held the most promise. Now he concentrated his efforts on the development of an artificial nesting site that would be of practical use to the average farmer. The problem was to provide the site with a foolproof system for maintaining the subsurface moisture essential to the bee's existence.

In collaboration with W. P. Stephen of the Oregon State faculty, Bohart finally found a solution. A three-foot-deep excavation is lined with polyethylene film, then backfilled with an eight-inch layer of gravel, topped with loam, mixed with granulated salt. Water is fed into the site through pipes leading into the gravel. The gravel layer distributes the water laterally, the salt helps hold moisture at the surface, and one watering usually lasts a season. The sites are colonized by planting them with soil-cores containing overwintering alkali bee larvae (*Nomeia melanderi*) dug from existing sites.

Since 1958, hundreds of these sites have been built by farmers, and there has been a marked increase in alfalfa-seed production in the areas where they are in use. Though many farmers still build their own, the construction of the sites has become an infant business in the Northwest. In 1963, for about $500 a contractor would build a 30-by-100-foot site accomodating 50,000 bees, or enough to pollinate 25 acres so thoroughly that a grower might easily have his yield tripled or quadrupled, increasing his income as much as $300 per acre.

The second major advance in wild bee husbandry came about partly by chance. In 1947 in Washington, D.C., a tiny bee a quarter of an inch long, previously unknown in this country, flew into the Smithsonian Institution.

It was captured and eventually identified as *Megachile rotundata,* a leaf-cutting bee native to the Iron Curtain countries. How it got to America, no one knows. But it obviously did not arrive alone for by 1955 others of the species were caught as far afield as California.

By 1958 it had become so abundant in the fields of Utah, Idaho, and Oregon, that Bohart began to investigate it. He found that as an alfalfa pollinator it had

The honeybee is more valuable to man as a plant pollinator than as a producer of honey

actually become the second most important wild bee in the region, surpassed only by the alkali bee. A series of experiments revealed, too, that the little bee would as soon nest in holes drilled in blocks of wood or, more surprisingly, in bundles of ordinary soda straws, as it would in its customary beetle burrows and old wasp nests.

This led to the design of a portable nesting box that can be set out on a post in the middle of an alfalfa field. The 15-by-20-inch box has 15 compartments, each holding 300 soda straws. A masonite panel slides into slots cut in the sides and bottom of the box to close off its open face when necessary.

To obtain bees, a grower sets out

"trap lines" of the boxes near the natural nesting sites of *Megachile rotundata*, waits until they become inhabited, then moves the boxes to his fields. When he sprays with insecticides, he can close his artificial nests and move his bees to safety. And in the fall he can store them, with their population of overwintering larvae, in a cool cellar until spring. The nests have been so successful that several companies have begun to manufacture them.

In addition to providing alfalfa-seed growers with the means to make better use of the two most valuable wild bees available to them, Bohart also has convinced a significant number that wild-bee husbandry also calls for greater care and discrimination in the use of bee-killing insecticides.

In some sections of the Northwest, Bohart said, this instruction has had dramatic results. In the Sunset Valley area of Oregon, for example, a farmers' association has been formed to protect bees from the indiscriminate use of insecticides. Those who violate the rules laid down for spraying fields are subject to fines. If this movement continues, Bohart feels that the miles he has crawled over insecticide-soaked fields, counting bee carcasses, will not have been in vain.

Looking to the future, Bohart said, "I'd like to see us begin to import foreign bees. There may be many species that would be as valuable to us as *M. rotundata* has been. Remember, most of our seed crops were introduced from other countries, where they undoubtedly were pollinated by local bees, many of which might well flourish here. What's more, we continue to struggle to grow some crops – beans and peas, for example—on the assumption that they're self-pollinating. Yet for all we know there may be dozens of bees in this world that would visit these parent lines and allow hybrid seed to to be produced.

"Take tomatoes, too. Our honeybees and most of our wild bees ignore them. As a result, growers of hybrid tomato seeds, for which there is a constantly growing demand, have to hand-pollinate their plants. It's expensive and it's time consuming. Yet we do absolutely nothing about it, even though we know that several species of wild bees visit tomatoes freely in Peru, the original home of the crop.

"This doesn't seem to make sense, which isn't surprising. On the record, a great deal that we've done and haven't done with bees these past few decades hasn't made sense. But maybe we've learned a lesson. Maybe we'll begin giving our bees a break." (*See also under Bee; Biological Control; and under Insect*)

—J.P.

Recommended Reading

All About the Insect World—Ferdinand C. Lane. Random House, New York.

The Dancing Bees—Karl Von Frisch. Harcourt, Brace Co., New York.

Destructive and Useful Insects—C.L. Metcalf and W.P. Flint. McGraw-Hill Book Company, New York.

The Insect Guide—Ralph B. Swain, Doubleday & Company, Inc., Garden City, New York

Insects in Their World—SuZan N. Swain. Garden City Books, Garden City, New York.

An Introduction to the Study of Insects—Donald J. Borror and Dwight M. DeLong. Rinehart, New York.

The Junior Book of Insects—Edwin Way Teale. E.P. Dutton & Co., Inc., New York.

Living Insects of the World—Alexander B. and Elsie B. Klots. Doubleday, Garden City, New York.

1001 Questions Answered About Insects—Alexander B. and Elsie B. Klots. Dodd, Mead & Company, New York.

The Wonderful World of Insects—A.T. Gaul, Rinehart, New York.

The World of Insects—Paul Pesson, McGraw-Hill, New York.

POLLUTION (*See Air Pollution; Oil Pollution; Water Pollution*)

POLYMORPHISM (*See under Egret: Reddish Egret*)

The pompano lives in the Atlantic, from Cape Cod southward and along the Gulf Coast. Only young pompanos are common north of Virginia

POMPANO
Other Common Names—Common pompano
Scientific Name—*Trachinotus carolinus*
Family—Carangidae (jacks, scads, and pompanos)
Order—Perciformes
Size—Length, about 1½ feet
Range—Along the Atlantic Coast from Brazil to northern Massachusets

The pompano's body is elevated, and compressed at the sides, and its forehead is steep and high. Its mouth contains many small teeth which fall out as the fish ages. There are two dorsal fins, the front one of which has spiny rays. The membrane connecting the rays is not present in older fishes. The rear dorsal fin is soft-rayed and quite long. It is very high at its frontmost end but drops off sharply. The anal fin is shaped similarly and the tail fin is deeply forked.

The fish is colored silvery blue with golden tints. Some of the fins have touches of orange.

The pompano's diet is mostly shellfish. It is considered a fine food fish and brings particularly high prices to commercial fishermen.

Some other pompanos include the round pompano, or permit, (*Trachinotus falcatus*); Paloma pompano (*Trachinotus paitensis*); and the African pompano (*Alectis crinitus*). —M.R.

POND

A pond is a body of water with a large shoreline zone and little or no deep areas such as one finds in a lake. The life within a pond is much the same in any portion of it, as the rather uniform sunlight, minerals, water temperature, and slightly variable depths combine to provide a uniform environment although even this can be subdivided into zones, in which different species live, from shallow to deep water.

Ponds may be classified in accordance with their formation. Temporary ponds, ones that appear with heavy rains and dry up in part of the year, support vastly different communities from those that are in existence all year round. Flood-plain ponds are often the remains of a former channel of a river (oxbows), cut off by a change in the river's course. Glacial ponds are those hollowed out by retreating ice, or represent the build-up of runoff water behind a dam of glacially deposited soil. Lime-sink ponds occur when limestone rock is dissolved by permeating water and collapses to form a surface depression. Beaver ponds are created by the dams built by these rodents around their stick and mud homes (*See Beaver*). —G.B.S.

Animal Life in a Pond

What a Pond Is

Ponds are small bodies of water familiar to many of us who see them over and over in our daily comings and goings. Some ponds treat the eye to rare beauty, others seem to be only reaches of mucky water. But any one of them can excite our curiosity, for all ponds have the charm of secrecy. The reflections upon their surfaces largely hide the world of activity that goes on below. They hide a population of plants and animals often far more numerous than that on the land near by.

In their watery surroundings these plants and animals meet living conditions very different from those on land and generally more favorable. Because of its density the surrounding water buoys up and supports their bodies. The shells of snails and crayfishes are thus less of a burden to carry. Water absorbs and holds heat. It likewise absorbs and holds the cold, so that changes of temperature do not occur as suddenly in water as they do in the air. (This makes the seashore a cool summer resort and much milder in winter than farther inland).

Less light passes through water than through the air but a pond is so shallow that at any point in it enough light reaches the bottom for plants to grow, except where shaded by the floating leaves of pond lilies, duckweed, or other cover. One of the main differences between ponds and lakes lies in the fact that the bottoms of ponds are well enough lighted to be inhabited, while those of the deeper and usually larger bodies of water called lakes often lack sufficient light. When the living conditions are good, a little pond, perhaps a hundred feet across or less, may hold an enormous population. One sweep of a net through the water weeds will bring up hundreds of animals, dozens of them large enough to be picked out with your fingers, and others visible only when the meshes of the net are examined with a lens. The more you look into a pond, skim it with a net from the shore, or wade about in it, the more you become aware of the abundance of life there, and the more you see the struggle for space and food that goes on within it.

Kinds of Ponds

In parts of the country where ponds occur at all frequently, there are more of them in spring than in August. Many of the spring ponds are entirely dried out by midsummer, or leave only mucky swamps behind them. These are the *temporary* ponds, the result of spring rains and melting snows; with no steady supply of water they come and go with the season. In some the water is re-

The edges of woodland ponds are alive with native mammals. Deer come to drink, and raccoons, foxes, and skunks wander along the shores in search of turtles' eggs, frogs, and crayfishes

plenished again in the fall, but in most of them it gathers only gradually before another spring.

The *permanent* ponds, those that contain a good supply of water the year round, are the homes of by far the greatest variety of life. They do not need to be large; some very exciting ones are not more than fifty feet across. They may be spring-fed or stream-fed, may lie in marshy valleys or in slight hollows of the uplands, and be heavily shaded or open to broad sunshine.

Life in a Temporary Pond

From late February, early March to mid-May, or even later, according to the latitude, temporary ponds are the resorts of animals that are dependent upon the water only a short time. The frogs stay in them until after the breeding period and then scatter over the surrounding meadow or woods (*See under Frog*). Toad and frog tadpoles remain until they change their form and become air breathers. Other residents of temporary ponds sink down into the mud after a brief period of activity, usually during the breeding season, and lie there more or less motionless until the following spring often encased in a capsule-like sac or cyst.

Neither spring peepers, *Hyla crucifer*, nor wood frogs, *Rana sylvatica*, suffer much if their pond lasts until July, for these frogs are the first to take to the water in spring and to lay their eggs. Both adults and young are usually out of the water by early July.

Among the most beautiful of pond animals are the well-named fairy shrimps. These delicate crustaceans (*see under Crustacean*) may appear in any of the smaller ponds, temporary or permanent, and though their presence is usually uncertain they most often occur in early spring ponds that change to marshes by midsummer. You may search for fairy shrimps in pond after pond, each of which seems the right home for them, without ever discovering one. Again you may find them in the very first pond you look in and perhaps repeat the experience for three or four years. After that they may all be absent again.

Fairy shrimps are worth searching for. The sight of their graceful movements through water strewn with broken ice is not soon forgotten. They are easily captured with a dip net and their swimming movements can then be watched at close range and examined with a hand lens. They must be kept in ice-cold water and even so will usually live only a couple of days in captivity. Fairy shrimps are about an inch long and varicolored – red, blue, green, and bronze. They always swim on their backs, the gills moving successively from the first pair to the last, so that waves of motion follow one another in quick succession from head to tail. Mating pairs swim about together for long intervals, the female above the male. She can be recognized by her position and also by the conspicuous brood pouch located just behind the gills. At first this holds the fertilized eggs and later the young shrimps, according to the date and the temperature of the pond water.

Through April and May, in the latitude of New York (in sheltered places even earlier), many a small pond swarms with the chestnut-brown, nearly full grown nymphs of mayflies (*Blasturus*). Their wingpads are thickened, indicating that the wings within them are already full-sized, although still much folded, and that their owners will soon be ready to take to the air. At this time they will rise to the surface of the water, shed their outer skins, including the seven pairs of gills, fly a short distance, alight on some tree or bush, and rest there for a few hours. Their new outer skin covers even the unfurled wings and looks gray and dull, so much so that *dun* is the fisherman's name for a mayfly in this subadult stage of life. After this first air-breathing period, the young mayfly sheds its skin once more and exposes the shining cover of its fully mature body. The adult has slender tailpieces which vibrate when it flies and have given it the name *spinner* (*See under Mayfly; and under Insect*).

Very soon after they become adult, mayflies join in a mating flight, usually in late afternoon or at twilight (*Blasturus* probably flies mostly in the afternoon). Then hundreds of spinners, nearly all males, swing up and down through the air in a rhythmic dancing flight over streams and lakes. They hold their rudderlike tailpieces stiffly extended and drop downward rapidly, sometimes thirty feet or more, to some point in the air from which they bounce upward as if springing from an invisible cushion. They continue upward in a vertical flight that ends abruptly and is followed by another swift descent. Thus they weave up and down, sometimes for a few minutes, sometimes for two hours. Then the dance ends and with it the life of the mayflies. Hundreds of them are strewn on the water's surface, helpless and dying. Here and there a female that mated during the flight now dips down to the pond surface and drops her eggs into the water. These hatch into nymphs. Some *Blasturus* probably live in the water till another spring, while other species will mature after about six weeks. The nymphs of still another species live in the water until their third year.

Adult mayflies are often called "Canada Soldiers." Canadians sometimes call them "Yankee Soldiers." Fishermen try to imitate mayflies in making their artificial flies.

Many other animals that are successful inhabitants of transient ponds are mosquitoes; water bugs, such as the water striders and water boatmen; certain snails, that can withdraw into their shells and seal themselves in during times of drought; and great numbers of minute animals, such as hydras and rotifers, that can live through a crisis in an inactive encysted condition.

Lurking at a pond's edge, a voracious dragonfly nymph captures a mosquito larva

A drop of pond water (magnified 1,000,000 times) reveals its multitudes of microscopic plant and animal life

Pond lilies are common floating plants that grow in water two to five feet deep

Life in a Permanent Pond

The most populus of the permanent ponds are those whose bottoms are composed of accumulations of the soft deposits of soil and organic waste brought by an inflowing stream, or washed from nearby slopes, and constantly created by the decay of plant and animal tissues. Plants usually grow well out from the shores of such ponds or entirely across them. Some of these plants, eelgrasses and water lilies, have stems and leaves several feet long. Countless numbers of microscopic plants, diatoms and algae, grow upon the bottom, in the surface waters, and upon submerged sticks and stems. These plants, both big and little, are the basic food supply of the animals. A host of herbivorous worms, clams, snails, crustaceans, and insects feed upon them and these in turn provide food for the larger carnivorous insects, as well as for the fishes, frogs, and turtles that prey upon them and upon one another.

Wherever plants are plentiful, various kinds of pond vegetation grow in zones parallel with the shorelines, and more or less characteristic communities of animals are associated with each zone. Three such zones are usually present, an inner, border zone of emergent plants, a middle zone of floating plants whose roots may be free or attached to the bottom, and finally the zone farthest out into the pond where the plants are completely submerged in the water.

The emergent water plants are closest to shore. These, such as the cattails and buttonbushes, grow with their roots in the water and their stems and leaves in the air. Among them are the reeds, bulrushes, and marsh grasses, and the arrowhead and pickerelweed whose white blossoms and blue spikes are a familiar sight in midsummer. In early spring, algae grow on the rotting, water-soaked plants and beadlike growths of green and blue-green algae form on old cattail stems. Later on, in April or May (depending on the latitude), water bugs, the water measurer (*Hydrometra*), and the water scorpion (*Ranatra*) lay their eggs on these stems. In this shallow zone it is easy to see that spring begins in the water long before it does on land. By February, through a window made in the ice, water boatmen can already be seen swimming about, and sow bugs (*Asellus*), crawling over the dead stems.

Above the waterline, the old cattail flowers, standing exposed to the winds, may be inhabited throughout the winter. The cattail moths, *Lymnoecia phragmatella*, lay their eggs in the lower pistillate halves of the flower spikes, and the larvae which hatch from them spin silken threads about the seeds, binding them together, thus making a shelter in which the builders are protected all winter. Flower heads in which cattail moth pupae are hidden can usually be detected at a distance, for they do not lose their seeds during the winter and look frayed out and much larger than ordinary flower spikes.

In the middle zone of the floating-leaved plants the water is from two to four or five feet deep. White and yellow pond lilies grow luxuriantly there; Elodea, a water weed commonly used in aquaria, and some of the many species of eelgrasses (*Vallisneria*) are common. The algae (*Nitella*) and the bladderworts (*Utricularia*) spread their vinelike growths through the water just beneath the surface. In some ponds great numbers of little duckweed plants (Lemnaceae) blanket the surface and effectually shut off the light from any plants that might be growing below them.

A great variety of animals live in this middle zone. Bullfrogs, the most thoroughly aquatic of our native frogs, as well as many green frogs, sprawl in the water with their heads thrust through the surface film. Yellow perch haunt these shallows and from March to May

Pickerelweed is an emergent hydrophyte that grows in shallow water close to the shores of ponds

lay their eggs in strings of jelly from two to seven feet long, twined about the water weeds. There may be many thousands of eggs in one string but probably comparatively few of the young fishes survive, since they are the prey of many carnivores—from dragonfly nymphs which devour them one at a time, to pickerel, *Esox niger*, which swallow them by hundreds.

Such weed-grown shallows are also favorite haunts of painted turtles, *Chrysemys picta*, which feed on the small animals that climb about on the submerged plants, as well as upon grasses and scraps of decayed plant and animal tissue. The two commonest pond turtles in the northeastern states are both easily recognized: the painted turtle, by the scarlet under rims of its upper shell, and the spotted turtle, *Clemmys guttata*, by its dark upper shell sparsely spotted with yellow. Turtles show the land animal ancestry common to many pond animals by frequently climbing out of the water onto anything that is afloat. Although these turtles eat freely enough underwater, they are rarely seen to feed when out in the air.

As soon as water lily leaves begin to be well grown they are gradually occupied by animals, particularly on their under surfaces. Colonies of freshwater sponges and bryozoans spread over them; snails feed upon the microscopic diatoms and algae that grow upon them; occasionally a scarlet watermite may be found there; also eggs in various stages of development and hatching, caddis flies, and beetles. As summer comes on, carnivorous insects become larger and great numbers of dragonfly and damselfly nymphs and the larvae of tiger beetles prey upon the young population growing upon the leaves.

The soft bottom of this region and the area extending out from it into the center of the pond (the third zone) also holds great numbers of organisms. The upper surface of the mud swarms with one-celled plants and animals, minute worms, and various small, burrowing animals. Among the larger animals that feed on these are the mussels and such burrowing mayfly nymphs as ***Hexagenia***, which are nearly two inches long when they are ready to leave the water. These nymphs occur in enormous numbers in many ponds and lakes and constitute an important food of fishes.

If a pond is overgrown with plants throughout its extent, the animal life of the border zones and the center will be about the same. On the other hand, if the center is a region of open water, it will be occupied by plankton, a literally floating population of millions of microscopic plants and animals that live just below the surface of the water. The plant cells of the plankton are so minute that many of them would go unseen in a glass of drinking water. Some of the animals are likewise minute, others are a little larger, and are many celled. All of them are transparent. Seen through the microscope they are objects of rare beauty. Because of their great numbers they are important in the food economy of the pond (*See Plankton*). —A.H.M.

[Editor's Note: Exploring a pond requires very simple equipment. Put on old clothes, take some mason jars, a pail or two, a kitchen soup strainer, and a homemade dip net—made by fastening a shallow bag of firm mesh (dish cloth suggested) to a heavy wire coat hanger bent to form a hoop and attached to a long mop handle—and go out to "fish." A few quick scoops with the net or strainer in reedy, marshy areas, as well as careful inspection of lily pad leaves, will soon fill your jars with an abundance of lively and curious creatures. Later, spread out your "catch" in white saucers of water to see how each looks and how it swims. By comparing the animals with illustrations in A.H. Morgan's *Field Book of Ponds and Streams*, many can be identified, and the interesting text of this book will acquaint you with their life stories. While num-

The male American toad inflates its vocal sac to produce a long, musical trill

bers of pond animals prey on each other, certain ones will live peacefully together and make unusual and fascinating aquarium "pets" for your nature room. Needless to say, animals cannot live more than a day in small saucers of water. After the aquaria have been set up, the leftovers should be returned to the pond or fed to the "pets" that would normally eat them. Caring for the inhabitants of the pond means daily acquaintance with their activities and habits. Thus the secrets of the pond, hidden so completely beneath the reflecting surface of its waters, are gradually revealed (*See Aquarium*)]

Recommended Reading

Field Book of Animals in Winter—Ann H. Morgan. G.P. Putnam's Sons, New York.

Field Book of Ponds and Streams—Ann H. Morgan. G.P. Putnam's Sons, New York.

Life of Inland Waters—James G. Needham and J.T. Lloyd. Comstock Publishing Company, Ithaca, New York.

A Pond in His Life in **The Wonders I See**—John K. Terres. J. B. Lippincott Company, Philadelphia.

Yellow pond lily

POND LILY
Yellow Pond Lily
Other Common Names—Spatterdock, cow lily
Scientific Name—*Nuphar advena*
Family—Nymphaeaceae (water-lily family)
Range—Florida to Texas and eastern Mexico, north to coast of New England, central New York, northwestern Pennsylvania, Ohio, southern Michigan, Wisconsin, and Nebraska
Habitat—Tidal waters, pond margins, and swamps
Time of Blooming—May to October

The margins of ponds, lakes, and inlets along rivers commonly harbor this summer-blooming yellow water lily. Although it may be found growing in company with the white water lilies it is usually much more common in waters that are somewhat polluted where the white lily will not grow.

The large, starchy rootstalk is anchored in the muck at the bottom of the pond and its long, rubbery stems are always longer than would be necessary to elevate the leaves and flowers to the surface of the water where they float. These long stems are nature's provision against the high water when the plant might be pulled from its moorings if the stems were shorter. The leaves of the pond lily have a waxy surface that water rolls off of easily, thus making the topside of the leaf difficult to wet.

Since the sepals are large and bright yellow they are usually mistaken for petals. The petals resemble stamens and bear the nectar. The large disk in the center is the stigma which ripens prior to the stamens that lie just beneath. At first the flower opens so little that visiting beetles, bees, and flies must touch the ripened stigma, leaving on it pollen from a previously visited older flower, before they can reach the nectar farther inside the bloom. The next day the flower opens wide and the anthers beneath the stigma expose their pollen. Thereby is cross-fertilization guaranteed. Later the many-celled, inverted, cup-shaped seedpod projects above the water. As the walls of the pod dry and crack the seeds are freed and float away from the parent plant.

The seeds of the pond lily are eaten by ducks to a limited extent and also by the Florida crane and the Virginia rail. The beaver, and even the porcupine, occasionally feed on this aquatic plant.

A few states have attempted to protect the pond lily by placing it on their conservation list.

POOR-WILL
Other Common Names—None
Scientific Name—*Phalaenoptilus nuttalli*
Family—Caprimulgidae (goatsuckers)
Order—Caprimulgiformes
Size—Length, 7 to 8 inches
Range—from Canada to Mexico, in the dry country east of the Cascades and the Sierras, following the arid lands across the lower Sierras down into Baja California

The poor-will is a nightjar, or goatsucker, names given to the group that includes the whip-poor-wills, the nighthawks, and the pauraque (*See Nighthawk, and under Whip-poor-will*). All are soft-winged, short-legged, insect-eaters, mostly flying at night. They subsist on flying insects, which they scoop from the air with the wide, bristle-edged beak. Courtship is at night, and the monotonously repeated call of the males is supposed to "jar the night,"

—G.B.S.

Voice in the Dark

The ability to remain hidden is possessed by a surprising number of animals, so much so that many of them are better known by their calls than by sight. This art of living unseen is not limited to the small or large but runs the gamut of sizes, from crickets to coyotes, with many intermediate species between.

As creatures that we hear oftener than we see, the various tree crickets, with their nationwide distribution, are prime examples. They can rub wings—vigorously in warm weather, slower in cold—and still remain hidden for a lifetime. Yet, eliminate the chirps thus produced and a garden at twilight loses a large part of its personality, solely by the removal of a customary sound, so faint, methodical, and monotonous that most people do not realize that it exists until after it is taken away (*See under Cricket; and under Insect*).

In a localized way the same loss would be felt if we should momentarily banish the tree frog chorus from moist woodlands; the pumping notes of a bittern from a dense marsh, and even the quavering whistle of screech owls nesting in suburban woodlands. Yet, with stealth, patience, and luck, these creatures can be seen, even in the act of making their varied calls—the frog with its ballooned throat pouch, the bittern with pumping body, and the owl with vibrating breast. But the poor-wills, birds best known as a mysterious voice in the darkness, are even more secretive. For many years they may not only defy one's stealth and patience, but seem to take a fiendish delight in calling from just beyond the rays of a campfire and then flitting farther into the darkness where their brown mottled bodies are lost to sight in mottled brown leaves.

Occasionally, while driving over dusty desert roads at night, one's headlights will reflect two spots of "eye-shine." If one travels much at night in the poor-will's country, he will almost learn to identify the owners of each pair of eyes by their reflected color. Thus, orbs of pale green usually have a cat or coyote behind them, while those that glow as silvery discs are usually those of a kit fox. So far, such identifications might be guesswork based on an affirmative majority, and only the pink glow of the eyes of the poor-will seems to be an identifiable certainty. Even in desert road ruts, blinded by bright headlights, the poor-wills remain true to their secretive character and after an instant of indecision, fly away with a mothlike flight.

There are four races, or subspecies, of poor-wills inhabiting the West. Those of the desert areas are light in color and match the glare of desert surroundings; those of the brush-and tree-covered coastal regions are dark to the point of being almost black. In a north and south line from southern Canada to the southern end of Baja California, Mexico, there are also geographical differences in color which form the basic differences in the races as ornithologists know them. Thus from Canada into Mexico and from the Great Plains to the Pacific, poor-wills exist by the untold thousands if their plaintive calls can be used as a measure of population. They are not rare in any sense of the word but their nests are found so seldom that to discover one becomes an event in the life of any ornithologist.

When they select a homesite, poor-

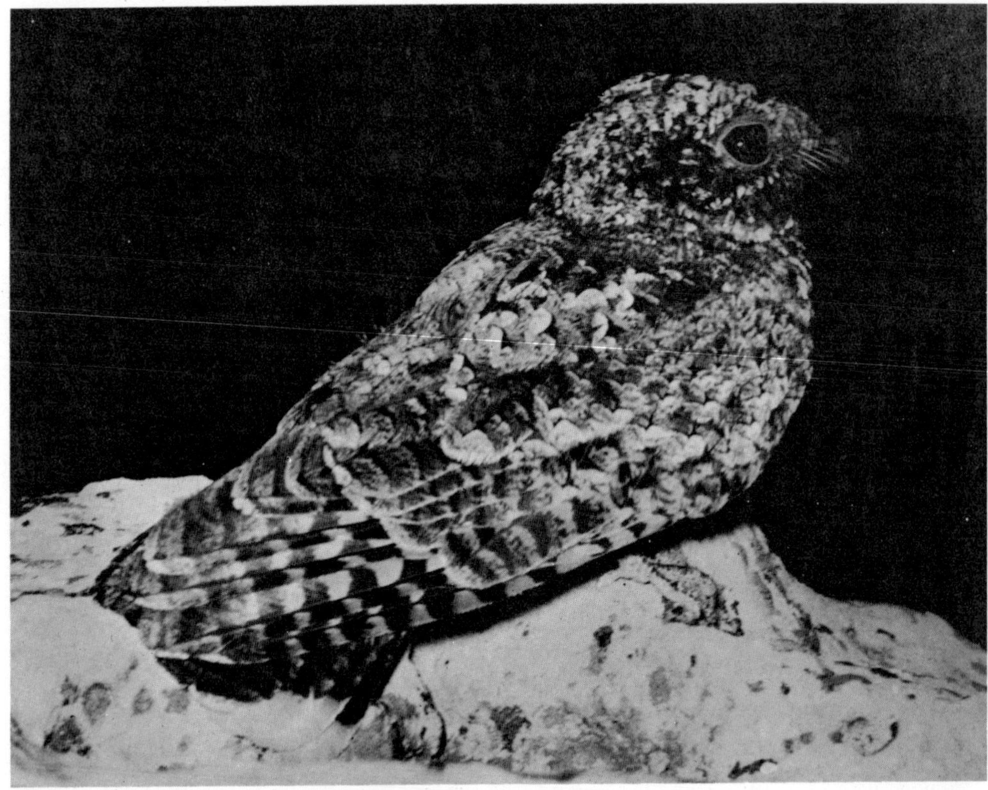

The poor-will is speckled with white and brown and blends well with its surroundings

wills make no attempt to build a nest, but instead choose a place offering some protection for the eggs, and, then scoop a slight depression in the ground. An uncovered nest with its two lusterless white treasures could not be overlooked by even an unobservant person but with the parent incubating it, the eggs are impossible to see. Home duties seem to change this bird from a shy, unapproachable voice in the dark to a fearless protector that stakes her all on a plumage of flecked browns and whites and the subtle blend into its surroundings that these markings produce.

It was during this seasonal characterization that the heavy boot of a naturalist-photographer unintentionally pushed against a poor-will and shoved her away from her eggs. For a moment she seemed to toy with the idea of recovering her treasures but then instinctive self-preservation got the upper hand and with a distinct hiss she fluttered to a clump of bushes about 15 feet away. There, spread in a ruffled manner on the ground, she simulated a broken wing and repeated this act time after time moving slowly away from the nest until she became lost in a thick growth of scrub oak. From the center of this dense thicket she uttered solicitous and anxious *werk werk* calls which were answered by another poor-will on a nearby hillside.

Thirty minutes after being practically kicked off her eggs the bird returned to land inches from the nest. Then, moving toward it on her inadequate, weak legs, she stumbled to it and took an incubating position. This was assumed in a drowsy fashion with wings loose at her sides and with eyes closed to mere slits. The feathers on her body were partially roused and with this disheveled appearance she melted into her surroundings like a drop of ink on a black blotter. Even from a distance of three feet she was difficult to see and separate from the rest of the area. On the ground glass of the observer's camera she so blended into her surroundings that he frequently had to lift his gaze from under the hood to check and make sure that there was still a bird among the sun-dappled leaves (*See Nature Photography*).

After several minutes of incubation a faint series of twin cheeps could be heard issuing from the nest, but it was not until the adult bird flushed at one of the photographer's motions that the source of the calls was discovered. One of the eggs was pipped and a faint note came from the hole in the shell. This in itself was not unduly strange as every naturalist occasionally finds these "talking eggs." But at this nest the photographer had his one and only experience of one egg answering another. Each time the unhatched youngster in the pipped egg uttered a chicklike *cheep* there would be an almost simultaneous call from the other unhatched egg. It was fainter and weaker, muffled as it was by the shell, but it was distinctly an answer nevertheless.

The following day the photographer noted that the precosity that was evidenced while the chicks were still in the eggs became even more apparent after they had hatched. Several minutes after the adult left at the photographer's close approach, the first chick that had hatched became frightened and left the nest in a surprisingly agile and purposeful manner. Short froglike hops of about eight inches carried it in a series of jumps to the cover of some dead brush about five feet away. When hidden to its own satisfaction it cheeped a few times and the other young one hopped along the same route until the two were again united.

Late that afternoon the photographer looked for the chicks but despite a careful search they could not be found. At the time he noted that he could almost feel their presence and he knew that he had passed within a few feet of this strange and mysterious family that was so admirably equipped to rely on natural camouflage. In a way their dependence on "blend" was similar to that of any one of a number of terrestrial mammals incapable of flight, which freeze, or become motionless, to remain hidden from an intruder (*See Protective Coloration*).

During the winter the calls of the poor-wills become a note of the past, or for an optimistic ornithologist a sound to be anticipated in the future. Like many other naturalists, one might be under the impression that these birds migrate southward when the colds of winter kill off their insect prey or force them into hibernation. This assumption has been strengthened on numerous occasions by observers seeing scores of pairs of pink eyes shine on the dusty trails of Mexico. These concentrations have always been seen in April, a normal migration month for the region. Later, an eminent western naturalist, Edmund C. Jaeger, brought to light a new and startling chapter in the life of this strange bird, a chapter that suggested that some individuals hibernate through the winter and forego the long flight southward (*See under Hibernation*).

Jaeger's observations started in an accidental way in the Colorado Desert's Chuckwalla Mountains. This area, parched and sunburned in the summer, begins to chill in late October, and from then until the following spring the myriads of phototropic insects drawn to light are reduced to only the hardier species. Insect-eating birds such as phoebes, swallows, swifts, and nighthawks, also seem to desert the area and thus Jaeger's discovery of a poor-will wedged in a small rock crevice came as a complete surprise. The bird acted as if it were lifeless and permitted itself to be handled and replaced in the crevice without making any attempt to escape. Throughout the next 85 days (from November to February) Jaeger revisited the spot at fairly regular intervals. During this time the bird remained in the rock cranny in an almost dormant state and did not vacate the spot until warmer weather again brought forth the hordes of insects.

This was just the start of a three-year study, for in the fall of the next year Jaeger again found the bird in its rock shelter. During the ensuing months his observations and research ranged from taking body temperatures of the sleeping poor-will to unsuccessful endeavors to detect a heartbeat with a stethoscope. This hibernation, coma, or dormant sleep, was so deep that a silvered mirror held before its nostrils failed to collect moisture from the bird's breath.

Jaeger's study definitely points to hibernation, something new in the bird world. Perhaps it is not so new to the Hopi Indians whose name for poor-will means *the sleeping one.* A Navajo Indian student of Jaeger's when asked where these birds spent the winter, answered, "in the rocks."

Bit by bit the strange life history of this bird is unfolding, baring the secrets of a night voice, a camouflage artist, and a winter sleeper all combined in one. —L.W.W.

POPLAR (*See under Cottonwood*)

POPPY

California Poppy

Other Common Names—Golden poppy
Scientific Name—*Eschscholtzia californica*
Family—Papaveraceae (poppy family)
Range—Columbia River, Washington to northern Baja California (including San Joaquin Valley)
Habitat—Sand dunes and bluffs along the California coast
Time of Blooming—February to September

California's state flower is the golden poppy. From burnished copper down

California poppy

through the yellows to nearly white, set in blue-green leaves, it makes a beautiful individual plant, but the glory of a golden blanket miles long and acres wide apread over the spring hills is a sight not to be forgotten. Especially in Kern County and San Fernando Valley are large areas of them to be found, even the deserts furnishing a diminutive species.

In the early stages the sepals are joined to make a tall, pointed "cap," the expanding petals literally rending it apart and pushing it off completely. Early morning shows only a glimmer of color through the mass of green, but before noonday they have flung their golden petals open to the sun and covered the hills with living fire.

These poppy fields were beacons to early Spanish mariners, being likened by them to a flaming altar cloth spread for a saint of Spain. The scientific name honors J.F. Eschsholtz, a German naturalist who accompanied the Kotzebue voyagers around the world in 1816.

Matilija Poppy
Other Common Names—Fried eggs
Scientific Name—*Romneya coulteri*
Family—Papaveraceae (poppy family)
Range—Santa Barbara County to San Diego County, California
Habitat—Arroyos and canyon floors, Upper Sonoran Zone
Time of Blooming—April through August

This regal plant is a perennial with a height of from three to five feet, bluish-green leaves, and juice that is colorless and very bitter. In May and June, in the washes and canyon beds of coastal southern California, come the exquisite flowers, each lasting but a few days. Six petals, shining silvery white and delicately frilled, five to eight inches across, appear as if fashioned from crisp, slightly crushed, tissue paper; the center is a high round ball made up of countless golden-yellow stamens. The fragrance is very delicate but marked. The expanse of white and the golden center have brought to it the common name of fried eggs. It is particularly fine in Matilija Canyon in the Ventura Mountains and in the vicinity of Corona. It is cultivated extensively in England where it makes a splendid showing on large estates.

Matilija poppy

PORCUPINE

Other Common Names—Hedgehog
Scientific Name—*Erethizon dorsatum*
Family—Erethiyontidae (New World porcupines)
Order—Rodentia
Size—Body length, 25 to 35 inches; tail, 5¾ to 12 inches; weight, 8 to 15 or up to 35 pounds
Range—Throughout North America including Alaska and Canada and most of United States (except the southeast) in coniferous forests containing poplar trees, especially the aspen

The porcupine is a woodland creature, frequenting most of forested North America. It is active the year round and at all hours of the day and night. Its unfortunate habit of girdling trees has, at times, made the porcupine a problem in some areas.

Armed with a bristling coat of some 30,000 barbed quills, the porcupine has made little progress along other lines of development. True, it has learned to climb and it feeds on the tender buds and inner bark of trees but its actions are at best slow and clumsy. Its evolution has been concentrated on the development of its coat of armor. Varying in length from one to four inches, the spines are loosely attached at one end to the skin of the porcupine. The "business" end of each quill is highly polished and needle-sharp at the tip, but about a thirty-second of an inch below the point are fine barbs directed backward that flare out, making extraction impossible without literally tearing the quill out. On guard, the porcupine turns its back to danger, bristling up a formidable array of quills as a preliminary defensive measure, but it goes into action with its tail when danger comes within close range. With this well-armed club it can lash a fast, well-aimed blow which on finding its mark drives a dozen or more barbed arrows deep into the victim.

Left alone, the porcupine does not look for trouble but goes its own solitary

The porcupine is protected by 30,000 sharp quills

way, often spending part of the day asleep under a log or in a rock crevice. When winter comes, several porcupines may congregate in one den, but some hardy individuals remain in their food trees even during blizzards. At such times they may remove enough bark from one tree to kill it, but usually their activities are scattered and damage is slight.

Despite its few habitual enemies, porcupines are rarely abundant in any part of their range, a fact probably due to the slow rate of increase. In early spring the female bears her single young, that is well-developed and already equipped with quills at birth. This baby porcupine has the distinction of being one of the largest, if not the largest baby born, when compared to the size of its mother. Having long survived the few bobcats, pumas, and fishes skillful enough to avoid its quills, only man is a threat to its survival as a unique member of the forest community.

PORPOISE

Atlantic Harbor Porpoise

Other Common Names—Common porpoise

Scientific Name—*Phocoena phocoena*

Family—Delphinidae (typical dolphins)

Order—Cetacea

Size—Length, 4 to 6 feet

Range—Atlantic coastal waters from Greenland south to the Delaware River

In many ways the common porpoise is only a miniature edition of its relatives, the great whales. A warm-blooded mammal, it is so well adapted to an aquatic life that it is often mistaken for a fish. With no external sign of any hind legs, its smooth-skinned body tapers into its tail, ending in a pair or broad flukes. The porpoise possesses a pelvic girdle, a framework for rudimentary hind legs buried within the musculature of the body. Its flipper contains bones in fingerlike form.

The mouth is simply a fish-catching

mechanism. Breathing is done through a peculiar single nostril, a crescent-shaped blowhole on top of its head, which closes under water.

The porpoise hears through a movable inner ear and periotic bone, and has the keenist auditory sense of any animal. It can stay under water for six minutes without coming up for air. But if it stays down longer it drowns as easily as a man. In motion most of its 30-year-life-span, the porpoise sleeps only in brief spells, partially submerged, eyes usually closed for 30 seconds, but sometimes for as long as five minutes.

Porpoises are fast; they have been clocked at 30 miles an hour. Scientists found that this speed is partially due to their skin, which is supported by a spongy mass of tubes and columns. This resilient material permits the entire body surface to undulate according to water turbulence.

The porpoise's body apparently assumes the contour of the water rushing past—matches the form of the waves. Unlike the rigid hull of a ship, the porpoise's shape, with the help of the spongy skin, adjusts in accordance with the pressure variations of the water around it. The result, *laminar flow,* reduces water friction drag by as much as 90 percent.

The single newborn baby is fed from two nipples set in grooves near the mother's tail. Contracting her abdominal muscles, the mother actually squirts milk into her offspring's mouth. Feeding every 20 minutes on milk 6 times as rich in protein as a human's, the young one increases its weight rapidly.

So complete in every other respect, the young porpoise has no teeth at birth; they begin to appear a few weeks later. Though it suckles for about a year and a half it begins to munch small squid at six months.

Schools of harbor porpoises are usually

Atlantic harbor porpoises

seen in bays or close to shore, occasionally swimming up rivers. They feed on fishes, including mackerel, menhaden, and herring. Their main enemies are sharks and killer whales (*See Whales, Dolphins, and Porpoises*).

PORTUGUESE MAN-OF-WAR
Other Common Names—None
Scientific Name—*Physalia pelagica*
Family—Rhizophysaliidae (jellyfishes with large, saclike pneumatophores)
Order—Siphonophora
Size—Float, up to 14 inches in diameter; tentacles, to 50 feet in length
Range—Worldwide in warm seas

The gas-filled floats of Portuguese men-of-war are a common sight on Atlantic beaches during a few weeks each summer. Bathers learn to dread them, as contact with the stinging cells in the long tentacles is painful.

The animals are related to the jellyfishes and are members of the phylum Coelenterata, that of the polyps. But whereas most polyps exist as either separate individuals or as similar individuals in one colony, within the order Siphonophora each apparent individual is in reality a colony of a number of them, with a division of function related to the welfare of the whole colony.

Portuguese man-of-war

The float is apparently one individual. Beneath it cluster a mass of blue polyps, one group with mouths, another that is composed wholly of tentacles with stinging cells, and a third whose sole function is reproductive. The tentacles kill the small marine creatures on which the animal feeds, the mouthparts swallow and digest it and pass a portion of it to the other parts of the animal, and the reproductive polyps turn out sperm and egg cells for the next generation.

The Portuguese man-of-war is sensitive to light and to water temperatures. It can alter its course to some extent, by inflating the float, contracting the tentacles, and drifting with the wind, or by lessening the float and extending the tentacles—always assuming that wind and sea may be moving in different directions. What basis the creature has for using these maneuvers is not known, but within a school of men-of-war it is not unusual to perceive individuals moving on several different courses. —G.B.S.

PRAIRIE

The great North American prairie was the region of high grasses in the Middle West that bordered the forested region of the eastern United States and merged into the drier, short-grass region of the Great Plains grassland. A small portion of Indiana was prairie, much of Illinois, nearly all of Iowa; the vast expanse of prairie extended south from Manitoba and Saskatchewan through the Dakotas, Nebraska, and Kansas into Oklahoma and part of Texas.

Typical plants of the tall-grass prairie are the big bluestem, switch grass, Indian grass, and slough grass (in wetter areas). The root mass of these grasses usually penetrates the first six feet of soil, bringing up the minerals, and manufacturing a rich, dark earth (*See under Soil Formation*).

Little true prairie now remains. The fertility of the soil, due to the original cover of prairie grasses, has resulted in

The pronghorn antelope has been greatly reduced in number by the destruction of prairie lands

its almost complete utilization as farmland and to the near extinction of the original plants.

Bison, antelopes, gray and red wolves, coyotes, foxes, rodents, prairie chickens, longspurs, and hawks were typical animals of the prairie, and their populations have dwindled with the extirpation of the grasses that supported them.

—G.B.S.

Passing of the Grassland Dynasty

Perhaps it is not strange that one may have garbled ideas of what a prairie is, for the true prairie of yesterday is gone. The magnificent carpet of grasses and flowers that stretched from the Middle West to the Rockies, from southern Canada to Texas, exists now in small isolated tracts. These are leaves torn from the pages of white man's conquest of the land. Corn has replaced the bluestem grass; the plains are plowed to wheat; cattle have edged out the bison. "What a thousand acres of Silphiums looked like when they tickled the bellies of the buffalo is a question never again to be answered, and perhaps not even asked," wrote Professor Aldo Leopold.

The prairie belongs to that vast natural unit of vegetation known as the grassland climax, which covers about a fifth of the earth's land surface. These grassland communities are all related and similar in the climate where they grow and in their ecology, but they have been split up into geographic subdivisions. The grasslands in Russia are called steppes, in Argentina they are pampas, in North America they are prairies (*See Grassland under Grass*).

When the English settlers first viewed the American grassland, they did not know what to call it, for they had no counterpart for it in their homeland. They named it prairie, the French word for meadow. If one could have driven,

100 years ago, across the flat expanse of Illinois, the swells of Iowa, the rolling plains and intervening valleys of Nebraska, the prairie would have unraveled ahead and on all sides. It was an association of plants and animals that were unique and distinctive of the vast grasslands areas, for the prairie covered more of North America than any other plant community. From relatively small scattered fragments of original prairie, plant ecologists have only recently pieced together its former range and structure. The common plant of the prairie was grass. Trees were absent, except along streams in its eastern half, and shrubs were scarce. Hardy prairie perennials belonged to some of the most diverse families in the plant kingdom, represented mainly by the grasses, composites, and legumes.

In the eastern part of the prairie the grasses were as tall as a horse and rider; in the West they were only ankle-deep. In the fall, prairie grasses of russet, purple, and yellow rivaled the flaming autumn of forested hillsides.

The flowering plants of the prairie that are not grasses are called forbs. Most of them are large and conspicuous, and they towered over the grasses of the prairie which fed countless herds of buffalo and antelope, and millions of hungry rodent mouths. The grass-eaters became the prey of prairie wolves, foxes, hawks, owls, and snakes. Prairie horned larks, meadowlarks, dickcissels, upland sandpipers (formerly called upland plovers), and prairie chickens were characteristic birds of the grassland.

The prairie plan of life involved keen competition for existence. In order that such a large number of plant species could exist together, it was "give and take." Soil moisture was absorbed at different levels, and light obtained at different heights. The taller plants shaded the lower ones, protecting them from the searing effects of full sunshine.

Animals were also adapted to a life in the open. There was no shelter from

Pronghorn

Sage grouse, once abundant in the prairies, are now limited primarily to the arid sagebrush-grassland and salt scrub deserts of the West

sun and rain, no trees to climb or hide behind. Animals, to escape their enemies, had to be good runners like antelopes and jackrabbits, or good burrowers, like ground squirrels and gophers. Birds were ground nesters. Keen eyes were developed to see prey and predator over vast reaches of land; ears were large to pick up far-distant sounds. Most bird songs and calls were louder and more far-reaching than those of forest relatives.

Some animals (bison and pronghorns) tended to congregate into herds or colonies (prairie dogs) to protect themselves against their enemies. Protective coloration helped them to blend in with their surroundings. Many of the mammals hibernated and most of the birds migrated to escape grueling winters. Many insects were almost completely inactive 10 to 11 months of the year.

The larger animals were mostly hoofed, grazing animals and during their evolution developed large ridged back teeth and long jaws that could move back and forth and sideways to grind up grasses and the tough leaves of forbs. They also developed a many-chambered stomach—an important adaptation for an eat-and-run meal.

Drier soils and less rainfall, increasing from east to west, molded the prairie plants into different combinations of grasses and forbs best adapted to particular regions. Three major associations were easily observable in a bird's-eye view of the prairie—tall prairie, mixed prairie, and short-grass prairie.

The tall-grass prairie, sometimes called the "true prairie," was easternmost, found in its highest development in Illinois, Iowa, and eastern Nebraska. The eastern margin of the tall-grass prairie pushed into Indiana and Ohio as a peninsula or prairie into a sea of hardwood forest. The tall-grass prairie received the greatest amount of rain and supported the largest number of characteristic plants, or dominants. Bunch grasses such as bluestem, spear grass and dropseed grew six feet tall or more.

Great numbers of flowering plants

seemed to outweigh the grasses in importance, but the grasses were still sovereign. The deep purple flowers of lead plant, the tall white fuzzy heads and yucca-like leaves of rattlesnake master, the brilliant red-purple spikes of blazing star, and the prairie counterparts of many familiar woodland plants—clover, phlox, rose, gentian, aster, and goldenrod—were there. These and many other plants might have earned our admiration for so much varied beauty and interest.

Farther west the tall grasses from the East and short grasses from the West merged, forming a distinct community made up of characteristic plants from both associations. This mixed prairie association formed a strip from Saskatchewan through the central Dakotas, Nebraska, Kansas, and western Oklahoma into Texas. Important dominants were slender grama grass, buffalo grass, and big bluestem.

The western and drier portions of the prairie extended from the mixed grass region to the Rockies. In this area, known as the Great Plains, the short grasses were abundant. Buffalo grass, bluegrass, June grass, and a wide range of herbaceous plants fringed the horizon.

Prairie will everlastingly mean "buffalo" to the ages. Gigantic herds—split up into clannish, matriarchal family groups—reigned over the entire prairie, even as late as Civil War times. Ernest Thompson Seton, an American naturalist, estimated primitive bison numbers at 75 million. Bands of millions migrated north to Canada in the spring and back again in autumn.

Buffalo provided the thunder of the grassland, and antelope the lightning. The graceful prong-horned antelope is the swiftest four-footed animal in North America, and can run 40 miles an hour or more if hard-pressed (*See Pronghorn*). Silvery gray jackrabbits, bounding along with bushy tails out straight, were conspicuous inhabitants of the prairie. Their stiff-legged, springy leaps of 18 to 21 feet carry them along at a speed close to that of the antelope. They live a solitary life, each animal dwelling in an area only about two miles square (*See under Hare*).

Rodents abounded in the prairie, outnumbering the larger grazing animals by far. Theirs was the life of the underworld — tunnels, nest chambers, and storage bins, which honeycombed the grassland from north to south and east to west.

Thirteen-lined ground squirrels were common throughout the prairie, but Richardson's ground squirrels, or flickertails, favored the short-grass plains. These sun lovers darted through the grass satisfying their omnivorous appetites, or sat bolt upright by their holes like surveyors' stakes. For more than half a year they lay dormant, sleeping away the wet and cold, emerging again with the coming of spring (*See under Hibernation*).

Pocket gophers lived the life of a mole, each in about a quarter acre of ground. They are about the size of a rat, with small eyes and ears, large front feet and fur-lined cheek pouches (*See Gopher*). Many species of deer mice and meadow mice riddled the prairie with their highways through the grass. They are active all year round and carry on their nightly wanderings under the snow in winter. The short-grass plains were covered with teeming towns of prairie dogs. These little creatures, which look like overweight, reddish-brown ground squirrels, stuck close to their own front yard, a scant half acre. Billions of prairie dogs, barking their feelings to the sun, were ever ready to dive headlong into their burrows, which often ran 14 feet into the ground (*See Prairie Dog*).

Dry, rolling land with its dense population of ground squirrels offered an ideal food supply for the badger, the prairie's "tough guy." With his compact, stocky body and strong front legs, the badger can dig so swiftly as to

The horned lark is a characteristic bird of both the tall- and the short-grass prairies

virtually sink into the ground where he spends most of his life—feeding, sleeping, and multiplying, or basking occasionally in his doorway in the sun (*See Badger*). Also living on rodents, the black-footed ferret, now very rare, was an animal of the short-grass plains. The black-footed ferret resembles a yellow mink with black feet, black tail and eyes. Its range coincided almost exactly with that of the prairie dog, for prairie dogs were to the ferret what venison is to the wolf (*See under Extinct and Threatened Animals of North America*).

The grazing animals, large and small, were inexhaustible dynamos, converting grass into meat for those animals that fed upon them (*See under Food Chain*). Ranging widely over the prairie was the gray, or timber, wolf, hunting in packs consisting of families or groups of families. The prairie wolf, or coyote, principally lived on the plains. Although the buffalo were too big for the coyote and the antelope too fast, their calves and the ever-present rodents formed part of its bill-of-fare. The barking and squalling of the coyote at dawn and dusk lent the eerie quality of true wilderness to the plains and prairies.

The swift fox was strictly a plains animal. The beautiful little creature, no larger than a house cat, lived in prairie burrows and seldom ventured far from these. Today, owing to widespread poisoning campaigns against coyotes and rodents, the swift fox has disappeared from many parts of its former range (*See under Fox*). Shooting, trapping, and poisoning campaigns have greatly decreased these animals, and all but exterminated the prairie dogs.

The population of prairie birds was composed of comparatively few species, but many individuals. As was true with the mammals, some birds were characteristic throughout most of the tall- and short-grass prairie.

Meadowlarks, horned larks, bobolinks, and dickcissels filled the air with color and song; grasshopper and savannah sparrows remained shyly within the grass cover; upland sandpipers, the prairie's shorebirds, were present in countless thousands; prairie chickens were the characteristic resident birds, their hollow courtship "booms" echoing in the dawn solitude; red-tailed hawks hung in the air waiting for unwary ground squirrels, gophers, and mice.

In addition to these, the lark sparrow and Henslow's sparrow, the long-billed curlew and Sennett's nighthawk were more often found in the tall-grass prairie; the burrowing owl, magpie, lark bunting, and several species of longspurs were characteristic of the short-grass plains. These are but a few of the most outstanding examples of the colorful avian population of the virgin prairie.

The plain's bull snake, prairie rattlesnake, garter snake, and common toad were frequently found in most places and during most seasons. Insects were abundant.

The boundaries of the prairie were not sharp lines, nor were they static. Along the northern, southern, and eastern edges, it gradually waned into smaller and smaller wedges in the surrounding forests. Trees and grass were perpetually locked in a struggle for possession of this no-man's-land, aided and abetted by the vagaries of climate.

Dry spells favored the encroachment of prairie into the wooded areas; cool, rainy cycles favored the spread and growth of trees and confined the grasses again to drier areas. The badger and other burrowing animals, in constructing dens near edges of woodlands, invited the establishment of shrubs, which in turn were succeeded by trees. Thus woodlands invaded prairie, and the prairie reacted to natural forces, spreading and receding, but holding its own until it came up against forces with which it could not cope—domestic grazing animals and the plow.

Agriculture has exchanged the prairie for pastures and cropland, erasing most of the original vegetation. The rich black soil of the tall-grass prairie eventually became some of the best agricultural land in the world. Those tall grasses that escaped the plow yielded to heavy grazing by cattle. The short grasses of the plains are able to stand up under moderate grazing, and still survive in much of the uncultivated area, but overgrazing destroys them. Too many cattle are now rapidly depleting the native cover of short grass, allowing the invasion of less nutritious bluegrass and many wholly unpalatable weeds and coarse plants such as sagebrush, prickly pear and other cacti (*See Grassland under Grass*). The increase of weeds has favored the increase of grasshoppers, rodents, and jackrabbits, which take further toll of the grasses.

Prairie, as a natural unit of vegetation covering a vast section of North America, is now regarded as a phenomenon of the past. The black soil of a cornfield is all that remains of the original diverse community, but there are still many small places, particularly along the edges of the range, where relict prairies still exist. Distinctive prairie flora and isolated typical prairie communities can be found in Kansas and as far east as Pennsylvania, as far north as Wisconsin and as far south as Kentucky and Tennessee.

In a few "waste" places—areas too rocky to plow, for example—native prairie grasses still bend stiff-necked in the breeze. "Worthless" areas along railroad tracks, which are burned periodically, are places where native prairie plants

Red-tailed hawk

have escaped destruction. Prairie grasses and forbs in graveyards, fenced and free from grazing and plowing, are remnants of the prairie.

The animals of the prairie have fared somewhat differently. It was inevitable that some should go, and perhaps surprising that some should flourish. The rulers of the kingdom were the first to succumb. Even the plains were not big enough for both the massive, impetuous buffalo and the land-hungry pioneers. The great beasts were slaughtered for meat and hides. Part of the white man's Indian-fighting strategy required the massacre of buffaloes to deprive the red men of food. The buffalo millions were reduced to 500 animals at one time. Now, living only in semidomestication, there are about 25,000 in the United States. Railroads and highways over rivers and mountains were often built over old buffalo trails (*See Bison*).

Pronghorns were mercilessly persecuted until they were almost extinct at the turn of the present century. These beautiful animals responded to protection and have been increasing in some western states.

The larger carnivores – wolves especially – were incompatible with man. Extensive shooting and poisoning campaigns have reduced them in many areas to a fraction of their former numbers. Naturalists and conservationists hope they never will see the West without a coyote, for the plains would lose much of their wildness and color without them.

Most of the characteristic songbirds of the prairie have adapted themselves to civilization, though many are reduced in numbers. The prairie chicken is one of the most fascinating birds of the grassland. Central Wisconsin is now one of the last good outposts of this scarce bird (*See under Chicken*). Overgrazing and man's stew pot made the upland sandpiper rare, but with protection and habitat restoration, this graceful bird with the haunting whistle is making a slow comeback. Hawks, eagles, owls, and snakes were persecuted until only a few cling uncertainly to their ancestral home.

The thousand acres of silphiums, which "tickled the bellies of the buffalo," have disappeared. The land is still there, people still call it prairie,

Cattle have replaced the herds of bison that once roamed the prairie lands

and it is still a land of sunshine and steadily blowing winds. One still feels its spaciousness—the endlessly rolling plains, the vast sky strung at night with stars so bright and close that one feels he can almost touch them—but the associations of plants and animals that made the whole prairie a distinctive community is now past history. Fortunately some prairie souvenirs are left—remnants of original tall-grass prairie and considerable areas of short-grass plains. The Nature Conservancy and other conservation agencies, several universities, and private individuals are joining to save the remaining North American prairies from destruction and are beginning to restore some areas to the original grassland community.

This is a job for all, which calls for immediate action. One can study his own regions and find areas worth saving. Landowners in the prairie states who still have some untouched grassland can set aside parts of their properties as living "prairie museums."

The prairie preserved and restored now will become part of the North American wilderness heritage. There the bluestem, escaping the plow on a rocky slope, the blazing star, shrugging off the cinders of a railroad track, and the brown-and-white flash of a pronghorn bounding along the edge of the plains, may still stir in our imagination the might and glory of yesterday's grassland dynasty.

—R.L.H.

PRAIRIE CHICKEN (*See under Chicken: Prairie Chicken*)

PRAIRIE DOG
Black-tailed Prairie Dog
Other Common Names—Marmot
Scientific Name—*Cynomys ludovicianus*
Family—Sciuridae (squirrels, marmots, and woodchucks)
Order—Rodentia
Size—Body length, 12 to 16½ inches; tail, 3 to 4 inches; weight, 1½ to 3 pounds
Range—Plains and foothills from southern Saskatchewan, Montana, and central North Dakota to south-central Texas, southeastern Arizona, and northern Chihuahua, Mexico

Up until the latter part of the last century, millions of prairie dogs inhabited the plains country, ranging north to southern Canada and west to the Rocky Mountains. The dog towns, as they were called, thrived in teeming millions. The prairie dog was as much a part of the West as the American Indian and buffalo. This familiar little figure, like the buffalo, has vanished before the advance of civilization. A few prairie dogs still exist in out-of-the-way places but nowhere is it permitted to maintain large colonies. The black-tailed prairie dog is the largest and best known and most abundant. The black tip to its bob tail distinguishes it from the white-tailed prairie dog, *Cynomys leucurus*, in which the tip of the tail is white.

Two other species of prairie dogs are recognized—the Utah prairie dog, *C. parvidens*, has a limited range in southern Utah, and the Gunnison's prairie dog, *C. gunnisoni*, inhabits southern Utah, southwestern Colorado, much of northern Arizona and the northeastern part of New Mexico.

Prairie dogs are gregarious by nature, and establish themselves in "towns," living close together much as fish travel in schools or as bees live in colonies. Each of these towns may cover several acres and consists of anywhere from 40 to 1,000 "residents." The reddish-brown, natural-earth color of the prairie dog serves it as a highly effective camouflage against its enemies.

The underground burrows in which prairie dogs make their homes average around 12 feet in depth, slanting almost straight down. The burrows also have numerous side entrances into which the animals can dart to conceal themselves even more effectively. To prevent water from running into the burrows the animals build, at the entrance, a cone-shaped mound of bare earth about one-foot high and three or four feet in diameter. With four-inch craters in the center the burrow entrances resemble miniature volcanoes. The prairie dogs form the craters by pressing the ground into shape from the inside with their noses.

The young are born during March and April, in litters of four to six and occasionally seven. After they are about seven weeks old, the young prairie dogs venture above the ground but dart back into the family burrow very quickly when frightened. The female apparently believes that suckling her young is a private matter. Any of her offspring's attempts to do so above the ground results in a slap that is anything but gentle.

As the youngster grows, it becomes a little bolder but still retains its tendency to scurry back underground when it senses danger. Being neighborly, it thinks nothing of taking refuge in another prairie dog's burrow if it happens to be nearer than its own.

Eagles, hawks, owls, badgers, snakes, coyotes, weasels, and other carnivores are the prairie dog's greatest natural enemies, but settlement, and the destruction of these predatory animals around the turn of the century led to their decline and the prairie dog's increase. The irrigated, cultivated land also provided the prairie dogs with plenty of food and water. With their populations unchecked, they devoured cotton plants, stripped entire acres of row crops, and

Formerly abundant, prairie dogs have disappeared from most of their original range because of extensive killing

rendered vast stretches of grassy rangeland useless to man.

The prairie dog's tendencies to compete with crops finally grew so widespread that they became a matter of serious concern. Local, state, and even national government agencies tried control programs to help farmers and cattlemen. The prairie dog eventually became a rarity.

In 1938, Lubbock Texas, created a prairie dog town. It is, perhaps, the only known project of its kind in the United States. Although a number of zoos and parks have prairie dogs, the Lubbock Prairie Dog Town is the only place of its kind in which they are permitted to live within a park in their native habitat. Lubbock is in the high, level, northwestern section of Texas, in

The prairie dog often sits upright

typical prairie dog country, therefore the "town" could hardly occupy a more appropriate site. There is an abundant supply of grass in the prairie dog town itself. Two-thirds of it are sown in Bermuda grass while the remainder is planted in rye for winter forage. To provide adequate irrigation the entire prairie dog town is equipped with underground sprinklers.

The rye and Bermuda grass are the only feeds provided by the park. The rest are supplied liberally by visitors who toss bread, cookies, vegetables, and other foods to the prairie dogs in much the same manner as New Yorkers feed the pigeons in Central Park. Sweets are a special favorite. So are the wild onions that have a tendency to grow inside the town. Prairie dogs are also known to be fond of the stems and seed-heads of sunflowers.

The prairie dog, though often inimical to man's economy, is nevertheless interesting, and so much an inherent part of the life and folklore of the western plains that it is certainly worthy of being protected and perpetuated for future generations. —G.K.

PRAYING MANTID (*See under Mantid*)

PRECOCIAL AND ALTRICIAL (*See under Killdeer*)

PREDATOR

In general, one animal that kills and eats another animal is a predator. The carnivores, or flesh-eating mammals, are well-known predators (*See under Carnivore*). Hawks, owls, eagles, and other *birds of prey* also are predators, but many biologists believe that even a robin that eats an earthworm is also a predator because it kills and feeds on another animal, even though it is a lowly worm. Many insects are predators in that they kill and feed on other insects (*See under Insect*). —J.K.T.

Predators and Predation

Predators—A Closer Look at the Killers

In desert or ocean depth, on mountain top or steppe or fertile prairie, in lake or stream or marsh or forest or cave, life follows patterns of encroachment and adjustment that certainly were established in their broader outlines long before man was present to concern himself about them. Apart from the refinements evolved by man, life is mainly a process of unimaginative exploitation of the exploitable, with the participants living as they can.

It is unfortunate that man, the specialist in evil, sees in predation among wild animals so much evil that is not there. Predation as a phenomenon is as nearly worldwide as any way of life followed by organisms. It is the only way of life that multitudinous animals—from microscopic protozoa up to the great whales—are adapted to follow at all. It fits very naturally into the old, old patterns of life being maintained somehow, when and where, they can be (*See Balance of Nature*)

The moth larva that bores through an apple isn't doing anything so much different from what a wasp larva may do in the body of a caterpillar or what a robber fly does when it pokes its mouthparts into a grasshopper. The reindeer

A stink bug spears a moth larv

browsing on a tundra does not succumb to temptation when it eats the eggs in a duck nest—it is just eating. The raccoon eating fallen plums has no reason to think that it shouldn't eat the newborn litter of rabbits that it may find at the same time—or to dig crayfishes out of their holes or to pursue a crippled bird that does not want to be caught.

Turkeys may feed upon large insects—and also upon small snakes if they can catch them, or possibly upon the eggs and fledglings of small birds. Or the predation may be highly specialized, a species of predator living exclusively upon one species of prey. The Everglade kite has a beak enabling it to extract a particular kind of large snail from its shell. The goshawk has some specialization in its short, rounded wings, by which it can "sprint-fly" through brush in pursuit of a dodging bird, but it also can and does prey upon mammals. Unlike the goshawk, the peregrine falcon is adapted for swift and sustained pursuit through open air and seldom, if ever, catches its prey in brush or on the ground. The great horned owl is a very general feeder upon nearly everything catchable from insects and spiders to skunks and geese, yet no one examining its soft flight feathers would call it an unspecialized bird. Likewise, the wonderfully keen noses of members of the weasel and dog families may be considered a real specialization for their ways of living, irrespective of how general their food habits may be.

In considering predation as a phenomenon, it should not be forgotten that the animals pursued, or preyed upon, have adaptations, as well, and that many of those suffering the heaviest predation have lived with their predators for some millions of years—and not solely because of their own high breeding rates. Wild animal predators are by no means always able to take their prey exactly as they may wish. Except for the more special of special cases, the records from careful investigations have brought out over and over again that the one big thing that determines what shall be preyed upon is *availability.* Nature shows scant favoritism in dealing with her creatures. The exploitable is exploited by about whatever can do it.

For extremely abundant small forms—teeming populations of insects or fishes, sometimes of mice, lemmings, or rabbits—availability may mean their local or regional, abundance. As long as these great abundances prevail, practically all animals having appetites and the ability to capture these "prey animals" can take them virtually at will. Upon the larger or less numerous animal life, predation may be or may not be so closely dependent upon abundance, but it is still linked with availability of prey.

One can recognize, of course, that animal life feeds upon something or it does not keep on living, and, if that "something" is not plants, it has to be animals. But, what about the sorts of predation that come close enough to people to arouse questions as to whether they should intervene, and, if so, how much?

If one lives in town he may know that the owl-roosts in the pine or cedar grove have bird remains under them and that those remains include more than the unwanted starlings and house sparrows. A sharp-shinned hawk or small Cooper's hawk may wrestle all over the lawn with a flicker that is almost too strong for it to manage, and then the hawk may sit there with outspread wings, taking bites out of the struggling victim. A squirrel may be seen carrying away something fluffy that is *not* an acorn, or a bull snake with bulges along its sides may lie under the bushes while the neighborhood birds flutter around it, or our pet chickadee may no longer show up at the suet, or there may be piles of feathers that we can't fully account for but we suspect . . . .

If one lives in the country, he may note that a red-tailed hawk is interested

A barn owl holds its furry prey with a strong, curved beak

in the poultry yard, and one need not delude oneself that it is after a rat if it can get its talons into one of those expensive friers. There may be raccoon or opossum or skunk tracks in the dust behind the coops. There may be a covey of nine bobwhites coming to the buildings during a late January snow and only five when next one sees them. Something predatory may be visiting the mourning dove nests in the grove, or one may see a snapping turtle feeding on a duck down at the pond, or the grouse or pheasants or rabbits or squirrels may never become anywhere nearly as numerous as they should.

Domesticated species can be so inept about protecting themselves or escaping predators that predation upon them falls in a very different category than predation upon the usual run of nature-tested wild mammals and birds. The poultryman has as much real cause as anyone to worry about losses he may suffer from predation, but even he may often greatly reduce his losses without much if any direct campaigning against the predators. Perhaps this may be accomplished through intelligent selection of a location or through improvement of housing, perhaps through something as simple as keeping an active dog to scare away foxes, or by providing shelters for chickens to run under, if attacked by hawks. An enlightened game breeder whose pheasant pens were being raided by eagles he was most reluctant to kill, stung the eagles with small shot at long range until they learned to stay away.

A tremendous amount of field research has been done on a number of North American wild mammals and birds. The resulting literature has brought out substantial evidence that looks incompatible with several of the earlier concepts of predation as a factor limiting populations of prey species.

Some predation *can* cut into populations, with the net result of there being fewer prey animals maintaining themselves. This may be conspicuously the case when the predator is an enterprising exotic or introduced animal with which its prey lacks experience. On the other hand, a surprising amount of predation upon our favorite game species or songbirds is upon "spilled milk," which has no real chance of being other than wastage, whether it is eaten by flesh-eaters or not.

For at least those common mammals and birds that have definite ideas as to property rights and the degree of crowding that they will put up with, their populations and rates of annual increase may be more or less self-limited. The fights between robins on the lawn, much of the singing or calling of birds during their breeding season, the pulling off of coveys of quail by themselves, and the many demonstrations of intolerance on the part of this or that species can all signify with varying degrees of emphasis something that, as realists, people should remember: Essentially, there is room only for about so many of what the animal behaviorists call a *territorial species*, in a particular area, at a particular time.

The "threshold of security," or supporting capacity of an area for a territorial species, should properly be thought of in a relative sense. Its values, expressed numerically, may differ with the year, and with the time of year, and, in addition, with the state of the environment. For our long-studied bobwhites, grouse, pheasants, and muskrats of the north-central States (Illinois, Indiana, Iowa, Michigan, Minnesota, Missouri, Ohio, and Wisconsin) threshold values, or supporting capacity of environments, have seemed to be generally lowest during or near the years ending in sixes and sevens, and highest during or near the years ending in ones or twos. Just what is behind these and many other cyclic manifestations scientists do not know. During a given year, threshold values tend to be highest in late summer or early fall, after the breeding season is over; lowest in spring, with the onset of a new breeding season and its new tensions; and intermediate in winter, when the habitat is neither so comparatively unrestricted as in late summer and early fall, nor so full of assertive competitors, as in spring.

There are deadly climatic emergencies —sweeping die-offs, for example—but the factors that genuinely govern populations may still operate with a good deal of constancy. The "ceilings" of individual bobwhites or muskrats to be accommodated in an area may remain very similar for years at a stretch, and the year-to-year population responses may then follow mathematical patterns. Especially informative is the frequency with which a prey population may increase in conformity to a definite curve, with little or no deviation that can logically be attributed to variations in kinds and numbers of predatory enemies nor to actual predator pressures upon the prey. These instances illustrate the fundamental independence that many prey species may show toward predation as a

A king snake swallows a whiptail lizard head first

limiting factor, even when the predation may account for colossal numbers of individuals or of large proportions of the prey populations.

Almost anyone who carries on intensive life history observations of common mammals and birds may find them preyed upon, sometimes quite severely, at immature stages. If a scientist sees litters of muskrats, marked for later identification, or broods of quail or pheasants or ducklings shrinking away, and at the same time, saw their remains at the feeding places and in the droppings and pellets of local predators, he could understand the feeling of despair that people might feel while witnessing losses suffered by species in which they had special interests.

But whether anything is done to give the species preyed upon added protection or not there is no justification for the emotional intemperance that one creature, killing another, often arouses in people. After all, the broods of small to medium-sized hawks and owls shrink away in a similar manner. Why is it so widely believed that predators do not have their own losses from predation? In fact, nothing suffers more downright severe "natural" killing, or predation, in relation to their numbers than do weasels. Still, if weasel numbers are controlled by this predation, it would seem to be mainly in the poorer environment, for weasels. In their better environment, weasel numbers appear to be determined more by the limits that weasels tolerate among themselves than by what may or may not prey upon them.

In analysis, predation upon most well-studied species of wild mammals and birds is borne notably by parts of populations that try to live under a handicap. If discovered by a predator, an unguarded clutch of eggs or a helpless litter is more vulnerable than the young that can scamper off and hide, and the less advanced young are more vulnerable than the strong fliers and runners or the ones that can fight back. Predation upon such ailing, weakened, or crippled individuals as one may loosely term "the unfit," does occur, but most of the thousands of victims of predation have the appearance of being physically normal for their ages. One who looks for obvious physical handicaps in the animals preyed upon may expect to find them only now and then. Exceptions may be those prey species that happen to be all but immune to predation. Even so, among these, the very young, the very old, the very ill, or the very unlucky, may not escape predation.

Handicaps imposed by circumstances may so often underlie availability to predators that it may be hard to find examples of victims that clearly were *not* members of biological surpluses or of parts of populations evicted by poor environments or environments already filled to capacity with their own kind, or otherwise made vulnerable by emergencies. When there is, in effect, a place for only about so many individuals of a species to live—for reasons of either or both environmental limitations or psychological peculiarities of the species-and when more than that number try to live there, tragic events have ways of befalling the excess populations.

In animals as dissimilar as bobwhites and muskrats, predation may be invited by overflows of populations into unfavorable habitat or by increased tension and friction in the social structure, even of individuals occupying the best habitats. Remains of the dead and "sign" of wholesale murders may be scattered about the landscape for a time. But, after nature's period of shaking down to comfortable or manageable population limits is over, both the bobwhites and the muskrats may live with remarkable security for months, even in the presence of large numbers of such formidable predators as horned owls in bobwhite range and minks in muskrat range.

With increasing knowledge of these natural interplays, one can hardly avoid being impressed by the automatic ways

A fox holds a cottontail rabbit in a strong grip

in which they work—always within the rules of order imposed by protoplasm and its environment. Common predators switch from one type of prey to another, in keeping with the outstanding role of availability which determines their food habits. Common prey animals, in their turn, show many types of population counterbalancing.

If predation by minks upon muskrats or by horned owls upon bobwhites is heavy, losses from other enemies tend to diminish in proportion; in the absence of the minks or the horned owls, losses from other animals preying upon muskrats or bobwhites tend to increase. The muskrats, themselves, can be the greatest killers of other muskrats in places lacking their typical predatory enemies. And, if losses of early-born young are unusually severe, there may be, in compensation, not only prolonged late breeding but also high rates of survival of the late-born young. Conversely, if losses of early-born young are unusually light, the season's breeding may not only cease early but the loss rates of the late-born may also be exceedingly high, and so on.

While it does not always happen that all loss from predation or from any other cause of death to prey animals is wholly compensated, at any one time or ever, far more natural compensating occurs

A horned owl returns to its nest with a pocket gopher

than people are in the habit of thinking. That is the supreme reason why so many prey species may thrive despite one's misgivings or expressed wonder that they can exist at all under the pressure put upon them by predators.

Instead of taking it for granted that the eating of an egg or the killing of a young animal by a predator must mean one less of the prey species to be around by the opening of the hunting season or one less for the next year or the like, one should keep in mind that such loss from predation may be chiefly a symptom, occurring incidental to some of the things that really dominate populations.

The great fascination of animal predation as a subject for study lies in the variety of its manifestations of the timeless laws of life. Predators are among those wild creatures that maintain their integrity as wild creatures regardless of human meddling and man's ridiculous propensity for judging wildlife as good or bad according to moral standards of his own invention that he hardly pretends to adhere to, himself. Many predators are surely among the wildest and freest of all creatures. Of our native wildlife, the predators, too, include some of the rarest, the most beautiful and the most superbly adapted animals. To some people they offer highly regarded antidotes to the banalities of a civilization top-heavy with people. (*See also Owl: The Habits of Owls*). —P.L.E.